D0004592

North to the Unknown

The Achievements & Adventures
of David Thompson

North to the Unknown

THE ACHIEVEMENTS & ADVENTURES
OF DAVID THOMPSON

By

Hubert Evans

ILLUSTRATED BY RUTH COLLINS

McCLELLAND & STEWART LIMITED
TORONTO   CANADA

PRINTED IN THE UNITED STATES OF AMERICA
AMERICAN BOOK–STRATFORD PRESS, INC., NEW YORK

David Thompson
"Koo-Koo-Sint"

At thirteen a London charity boy . . .

At seventeen leading his own party into the Blackfoot country. . . .

Staunch friend of Indians, fur trader and explorer, David Thompson was destined to be called *"the greatest land geographer who ever lived."*

As a youth, hardship, danger and jealous opposition were his lot. Largely self-taught, he mastered his craft the hard way. Still in his twenties, he fixed the source of the Mississippi, mapped much of Lake Superior, the Canadian North and several rivers of the West. His map of the upper Columbia is still "official" in the United States and Canada.

"Koo-koo-sint," his Indians named him—"The Man Who Looks at the Stars." And by his daring and his loyalty to truth—no matter where it led him—this boy of the London slums came close to reaching them.

North to the Unknown

*The Achievements & Adventures
of David Thompson*

CHAPTER ONE

AT ST. SAVIOUR'S DOCK, close
by London Bridge, where the Hudson's Bay Company ship
Prince Rupert lay, all was confusion. As with most deep-
water sailings, no matter how well planned, there was the
usual last-minute haste—seamen shouting and heaving; bales
and casks, blacksmiths' supplies, trade goods and personal
belongings being swung aboard with little time for proper
stowage; company officials in ruffles and breeches bustling
about importantly and getting in each other's way. It was
May the twentieth and the year, a troubled one, was 1784.

1

David Thompson jumped down from the cart which had brought him and his poor belongings from the Gray Coat Charity School and, with the carter's help, got his box to the gangplank where he was struggling to get it on his shoulders when a young sailor, bare to the waist, vaulted the rail and ran to help him.

"I'm Jem Little, 'prentice seaman," he explained. "Orders are for you to share the cabin with me, for'ad. Let's get your chest aboard and stowed. You'll be wise to keep from underfoot. These quill-pushing poppycocks from the company office have put the master in an evil humor. Old women, the pack of them, with their chatter and last-minute orders. If we don't step lively, we'll miss the tide."

A few minutes later, as best he could, David was stowing his belongings in the lockers of the cuddy where the young seaman had left him. They were few enough for a boy committed to seven long years overseas; a new coat and breeches of his mother's own home-spun, the woolen vests and stockings she had knitted him in preparation for the Arctic cold; and wrapped in an old jacket his precious books on mathematics and navigation, along with the Bible the headmaster had inscribed this morning and given him when the last good-byes were being said.

Fortunately that parting scene had been a brief one. Old Bones, the servitor, gruff as ever, had ordered Geordie Charles and another boy to help David with his box. And when he was aboard the waiting cart, the group of Gray Coat boys under the ancient gateway had crowded around to shake the young adventurer's hand and wish him well. Bonds were strong, for with parents either dead or in Debtors Prison or in such poverty that family life was impossible, most of them knew no other home.

"Keep an eye cocked for Jennings and Alf Robinson," one of them called out as the driver lifted his reins. "Jennings

2

could always look out for number one. But poor old muddle-headed Alf! Like as not by now he's scalped."

"No matter," Geordie joked. "What's one Gray Coat boy more or less? There are more where they come from."

"If they don't vanish into thin air the way Sam McPherson did," a boy had jested. "He's the first Scotsman I ever knew who wouldn't at least wait to collect his wages."

That mention of wages was taken for what it was meant to be—a joke. And to David, as the cart had driven off, it was a bitter one. Even a few shillings to buy some parting present for his widowed mother would have helped. But the Honourable Company of Gentlemen Adventurers of England Trading into Hudson's Bay did not pay its apprentices wages. Instead, the Gray Coat Charity paid the company five pounds to take even an ambitious lad like young Thompson off its hands. And as for Sam's disappearance, well, that was a mystery never likely to be solved. Sam had always been a moody, unpredictable fellow but, still and all, it would have meant a good deal, David thought, if with the articles for both of them all duly signed, they could have been starting for the New World together this morning.

In spite of the commotion outside, David paused a moment before going out on deck. From his earliest years he had possessed the faculty of intense concentration, of being able to shut out from his mind all distracting sights and sounds. It was a faculty which was to serve him well in many a crisis of his life. And now, as he had been taught to do, he committed himself and those he loved to his Maker's keeping.

When he came on deck, the *Prince Rupert's* spars were beginning to move slowly past the grimed fronts of buildings on St. Saviour's Dock. A widening gap of water showed between ship and shore. It was a gap which, for David Thompson, would never close, for though his eyes would be the first to see vast stretches of a continent, the grimy streets of London town would never pass before his sight again.

Aided by the ebb tide, the *Prince Rupert* floated down the Thames and by the following afternoon her close-hauled canvas had filled to a beam wind and she was moving northward with the low Essex coast on her port quarter. Late that night a heavy North Sea groundswell began and from his berth David could hear the complaint of straining blocks aloft. As he was dropping off to sleep, Jem Little came off watch. The ship's nose was sousing into the swell so violently that David wondered how his cabin mate could keep his feet.

"I dare say you get it a good deal worse than this most voyages," David commented, propping himself securely on his elbow, his back against the bulkhead.

Jem grinned. He was a tallish, tough-fibered sort, the mark of the sea already upon him. "A chap gets used to it. For my part, I'd take it a thousand times over rather than what you're going to out there."

"What's it like?" David asked with suppressed eagerness. The far places had always held a strong fascination for him but, well founded as was the Gray Coat School, libraries for boys were unheard of in eighteenth-century England. Books were scarce, and dear. Only a few worn copies of *Robinson Crusoe, Gulliver's Travels, Sinbad the Sailor* and similar classics passed from hand to hand among the Gray Coat boys. But this young sailor knew the world at first hand.

Jem shrugged. "Every man to his liking. Me, I want the heave of a deck beneath my feet."

"The land out there, great forests, rivers? And the Indians, tell me about the Indians."

"Indians won't ever bother me. Or you either, if they're

4

all like those around the posts, Churchill, York Factory and the like. A thoroughly browbeaten lot they are, to my way of thinking." Jem drew off his sea boots and sprawled in the bunk opposite, his lean, strong forearms behind his head. "Tastes differ, though. Mr. Prince, the sloopmaster at Fort Churchill, he used to be one of our ship's officers and he vows he likes it. He's a good sort, Mr. Prince. You and he should hit it off." Jem stared at the deck beams a moment. Then he glanced at the empty bunk above David's. "I wonder will it ever be known what became of *him?*"

The glance told David it was Sam McPherson that Jem was thinking of.

"I heard the officer of the watch and the bosun talking when I took my trick at the wheel tonight," Jem went on soberly. "It'll go hard with your friend if ever the law catches him. Desertion, they're calling it, him being articled and all. It'll be penal servitude—or worse." Then after David had made no show of answering: "Well, I'm off to sleep. Northeaster making and they'll be turning out all hands before I've had my forty winks."

How much did Jem Little know? How much did any of them know? David asked himself as he lay in the darkness and listened to the creaking of the heavily-laden ship. No one, neither the headmaster at the school nor the irate company officers, had questioned him as to what he knew of Sam McPherson's disappearance. And until they did—

Of all the boys at Gray Coat School, Sam was the only one who had persistently discouraged all close friendships. He had no liking for sports and while he had a good enough head on his burly shoulders, that moody stare and the thick, often sullen lips had made more than one of the masters put him down as obstinate and even insolent. And, yet, because

5

he and David had been fated to go out into the world together, he had, of recent months, revealed a preference for David's company.

David's thoughts kept going back to the evening of the day the headmaster had sent for them to say the great company wanted them. The boys detailed to serve the evening meal had moved the forms out from the walls of the common room and laid out the mugs and pewter basins on the long deal tables. The night was chill, with a clinging fog, and there were extra coals for the fire. As the boys crowded around the hearth, three seniors who had managed to elude old Bones in the fog that afternoon told of a public hanging they had witnessed near Tower Hill. "For stealing from a shop. A joint of mutton we heard people say."

But David had been of no mind to listen. As soon as the meal was over and the town ban lifted for the early hours of evening, he planned to run home across the river and tell his mother the momentous news. Then, at the last minute, Sam had asked if he might go along.

As they hurried toward London Bridge, the fog was like a shifting wall around them. The torches of chairmen jostling their way through the crowded, narrow streets shone eerily. People loomed momentarily through the murk and then were gone. Below, as they crossed the bridge, they could hear the shouts of bargemen along the river.

"Seven years is a long time," Sam had blurted out. "We may never see England again."

"Think of Jennings and Robinson," David had reminded him. "Only charity boys like us, but now in a fair way to be trusted employees of the company. Ones like us can better ourselves out yonder. What have we to hope for if we stay in England?"

"You heard what Bones said about the Indians?" Sam had answered dourly. "He said he had many a comrade

6

among the English redcoats was captured by the savages and never heard of again."

David chuckled. "That carrot top of yours would be a prize for any scalping party." Then soberly: "It's not the sea you're afraid of?"

"I fancy the sea. That's what made me like it when the masters put me into navigation class. I'd be well fitted for the sea. But this wild country! Why not call it penal servitude and be done with it?" Sam's voice hardened with sullen rebellion. "Have we committed any crime? Then why should you and I be herded onto their company vessel like it was some convict ship?"

David experienced a strange and disappointed pity, for he knew now that Sam McPherson, always ready to strike out at any boy who crossed him in the school, was a prey to fear, to his own dark imaginings. "I thought you'd be the last one to put so long a face on it," he said.

And instantly he would have given a good deal to have the words unsaid. "Go on, say it," Sam demanded harshly. "Say I'm afraid. Blab it to the whole school for all I care." Sam was all but shouting now. "But just because I stand up for my rights, because I won't toady—"

"Them's fine, fightin' words, me laddie-buck," a man's voice called out from the door of the grog shop the two boys were passing. "Not so fast. I want to talk to you." The man lurched forward and clapped a detaining hand on Sam's broad shoulder.

David whirled. In the sickly reflection from the grog shop window, he saw that the man wore his pigtail tarred sailor fashion. "Now here's a pair o' likely lads," the man went on with forced joviality. "Y' talk like ones of spirit." He winked knowingly. "Goin' to sea, are you? Well, now, what d'y' say to a little voyage to the Continent? Pleasure and profit both —and no questions asked."

7

David reached over and knocked away the detaining hand. "What way is that to treat a shipmate?" the man protested. "Like I was the press-gang. A civil question should get a civil answer, I always say. A pleasant journey by stagecoach to the Suffolk coast, a lugger that can show a clean pair o' heels to His Majesty's revenue cutter—the best o' them as ever sailed—and when the stuff's ashore, share and share alike as shipmates should. What say, me lads?"

David, moving away, was astounded that Sam so much as stayed to hear more. "Come on," he urged. "Why listen to his guff?"

"I'll listen long as I've a mind to," Sam snapped. "I'm my own master and—"

"Sam! You're not—you're not letting yourself be taken in by that?" David asked in real alarm. "What's the matter with your head? Think what it means!" He took a quick step closer. Who or what hit him he never knew, but when he came to he found himself sprawled in the gutter of the mean street, and Sam McPherson and his companion had gone.

Jem Little was just coming off watch next morning when David made his way, with difficulty, aft along the slanting deck. The ship was beating her way, slugging through the steep crests of a stiff northeaster. "You'll find your sea legs before the day's out," Jem encouraged as David joined him at the rail.

Eastward the sun, magnified by the dissolving fog haze, was laying broad avenues of shifting light on the tossing water. Aloft, the taut hollows of the canvas glistened with the clean brightness of the morning, and the exposed surfaces of the ship were sharply outlined with light and shadow. High above, gulls coasted, the undersides of their shapely wings unreal and lovely in the reflected light.

8

Having slept in his clothes, with his greatcoat over him, in the ill-ventilated cuddy, David felt he could the better enjoy his first morning at sea if he freshened up a bit. With Jem's help, he was about to lower a deck bucket overside and souse his head in the invigorating salt water when a shout from the lookout made both boys stare to windward.

Three miles away, two sails were bearing down on the *Prince Rupert* on a course which should bring them close to starboard. Then while they watched, a puff of smoke showed from the bows of the pursuing craft and in a moment the report of a cannon, muffled by distance, came down the wind.

Jem snapped his fingers and, leaping to the bulwark, held himself erect by the forward stays. "A lugger, a Suffolk smuggler!" he shouted. "And a revenue cutter giving chase. Swing up here beside me, Davvie, if you want to see a sight."

Running full before the northeaster, the two small vessels bore down rapidly, and the boys could see the shorn water piling white in the slanting sunlight beneath their bows. Then the cutter's bow chaser spoke again.

"A hit! A hit!" Jem shouted.

"A hit—my eye!" an old seaman standing behind them scoffed. "The shot came short. Did ye not see the splash astern? If His Majesty's gunners can do no better than that, the smuggler'll be showing him a clean pair of heels."

"But I saw his after-sail peak flutter and begin to drop," Jem argued. "Seemed like it was coming down. I thought the ball had cut his halliard."

"Use your eyes, lad. His spar's cocked. He's spilling nary a hatful o' wind."

And so it seemed to David. But, like Jem, he fancied he had seen the peak of that sail flutter and droop for a second or two.

Mr. Summers, the senior officer, had crossed from the weather side of the poop and was watching the chase through

9

his spyglass. "The lugger's in trouble of some kind," he sang out. "Leastways there's unseamanlike commotion on her deck. A scuffle, it looks like."

Hearing the gunfire, men off watch had come on deck and lined the rail to watch the sea fight. "By the powers!" the first officer shouted down to them. "Are my eyes deceiving me? Did any of you see a man go overboard?"

But now the smuggler's swivel gun had begun peppering away. The cutter's forward guns answered thunderously and in the excitement of the fight all else was forgotten.

By now the two small vessels had crossed the *Prince Rupert's* course a mile or so ahead. "Yon lugger's well sailed!" a man exclaimed admiringly. "If the wind doesn't freshen, she bids fair to get away."

"For my part, I hope she does," a bearded seaman answered. "They're fighting for their lives. If they're overhauled, 'twill be Execution Dock, most like. Or if they're luckier than most, they'll be pressed into the navy." He prodded David with a horny thumb. "Ever see a man swinging from the yardarm, lad? Well, ye have my word for it, it's not a pretty sight."

Presently, as pursuer and pursued were almost hull down to southward, the lookout in the bows gave a long-drawn-out shout. The breaking seas, combined with the myriad sounds of a ship laboring under a press of canvas, drowned out whatever it was he was shouting. But Mr. Summers must have either seen or understood. David saw him race to the weather side of the poop, the bosun's pipe sounded shrilly, summoning the watch to their stations. Then, with laborious, grudging complaint and reluctance, the *Prince Rupert* hove to and a boat was lowered.

Jem, scrambling higher in the foremast stays, shielded his eyes with one hand. Then he pointed and David fancied he could make out some small object as it rose to the crest of

10

a wave a cable's length to starboard. "A body! A floating body!" Jem shouted down.

As the ship lost way and the slatting of idle canvas filled the air with a confusion of sound, David tensely watched the rowboat pull away. By his reckoning, it must be close to where the two small vessels had raced across the ship's course, and if a man had fallen overboard from the lugger, his fate could have been no worse than if he had stayed aboard and fought it out with the law to the bitter finish. The rowers were resting on their oars now and he saw a man in the boat's bow lean over and haul a limp figure aboard.

All hands who could leave their stations lined the rail, and as the boat returned to the lee side of the wallowing ship David saw a sight which almost turned his stomach. Slumped against a thwart, half-drowned, and his face and one side of his head a hideous mask of blood, the rescued smuggler sprawled grotesquely. Before they hoisted him aboard, one of the seamen cupped water in his hand and tried to swab the worst of the blood away. David's heart seemed to stand still. He could not be sure. One ear seemed to have been slashed almost off and the scalp hung over it in a grisly flap. But that slack jaw, that matted, carrot-colored hair—

"Poor devil!" a seaman beside David growled, with rough sympathy. "He's little more than a lout of a boy."

Abruptly David turned away. The sight was revolting enough but it was not altogether that which made him feel he had to take a turn along the deck. He had to think, and think fast. There was not a shred of doubt but that the smuggler lying there like a dead thing on the deck was Sam McPherson. Sam, moody, always withdrawn, his hand against every man's, brooding over fancied slights, nursing his grudges—Sam had come to this! And yet Sam, with all

11

his faults, had wanted, if only for that short while, to be his friend.

"Step lively," the first officer was bawling as the ship threatened to pay off down-wind. "Don't leave him lie there like a stuck pig to stain the deck."

"Aye, aye," the boatswain acknowledged. "But where's he to be stowed, sir? Just say the word."

David hurried to where Jem was standing. "That spare bunk in the cuddy. Could he lie there? I've no duties aboard. I could look after him."

Jem darted up the ladder, saluted and spoke to Mr. Summers. Consent was given, the limp body was shifted onto a tarpaulin and borne to the cuddy forward.

"I doubt if he'll live," Jem said tensely when the others had gone. "All that blood he's lost!" He glanced at the gashed ear. "A swipe with a cutlass, and it fetched him fair. The wonder is it didn't lay his skull open. Like a broadaxe would a pumpkin," he added, the sight so moving him that he tried to hide his feelings behind this seeming tough-mindedness.

Already David was rummaging through his locker for some material suitable to bind the wound. Among his clothes he found the single linen shirt his mother had made for him from one which had belonged to his father. He began tearing it into strips.

"Aboard ship there's some that say Stockholm tar is good for wounds," Jem said. "I'll go ask the bosun to let you have some."

David knew that, no matter how he tended it, if Sam lived he would bear a disfigurement to his dying day. Proper surgery was still far in the future. Many who, like old Bones, had survived the war with the American colonies were to be seen in London streets with ill-healed wounds, though none, David thought, as disfiguring as this one. But he must do the best he could. Life was cheap, those times, and had the ship's master been on watch, instead of Mr. Summers, the *Prince Rupert* would likely not have been hove to for the sake of this piece of human wreckage.

What with the loss of blood and his long immersion in the cold sea, Sam McPherson was still more dead than alive. But in his unconscious state he at least felt no pain, and David made as thorough work as he knew how of getting the flap of scalp back into place and of staunching the blood still seeping from that ghastly ear. Then, covering Sam with his own greatcoat, he went on deck and watched through the open door for some slight sign of returning life.

Sitting there on the water butt, chin in hand, young Thompson blamed himself for not having interfered more strenuously that night the drunken sailor had waylaid them. But what more could he have done? Countless times since he had tried to imagine what had happened, and the more he thought of it, the more certain he became that some footpad or similar accomplice had, at a signal from the sailor, struck him from behind. Unpredictable and self-willed though Sam was, he certainly had not raised his hand against him.

And now what was to become of poor, blundering Sam? The *Prince Rupert* might break her voyage somewhere along the Scottish coast. She sometimes put into Portland Firth, Jem had said, lying at Stromness to make final stowage of cargo. Would Sam be sent south in irons from there, to face his trial and possible execution? Or would the master prefer making him work his passage to Hudson's Bay and back before turning him over to the authorities?

"One thing's certain," David decided. "How he got aboard that smuggler, or why he was struck down, is not my business. And for his sake, as well as mine, it will be better if nobody, not even Jem, finds out we know each other. Nobody's going to have me give evidence against him."

13

Sick at heart, he wondered if Sam was really going to die. For seven years he and Sam McPherson had lived under the same roof, eaten the same rough food, done their lessons at the same form. And now, to have it come to this! Until the headmaster sent for them that wintry afternoon, they had not been special friends. But from then on— So, scene by scene, memory led his thoughts back to the day it all began.

CHAPTER TWO

THE TROUBLED year was dying. The red brick walls of the Gray Coat Charity School were clammy with fog and the near-by spires of Westminster Abbey had been blotted out. From beyond the stone archway came street sounds—the rumble of carts, the shod feet of horses on the cobblestones, the shouts of chairmen and the high-pitched chant of a peddler crying "eels for sale." To the thirteen-year-old Welsh boy, David ApThomas, now called Thompson, they were familiar sounds.

"A fellow could get lost in a pea-souper the likes of this," Sam McPherson said as they stood under the stone arch.

"Lost? And us learning to be navigators? Tell you what,

15

Sam," David proposed. "If we could lay hands on that pocket compass they let us use in class, we could chart our course and find our way wherever we've a mind to in the city. What say we try?"

"*You* could," Sam said dourly. "You always did have a good sense of direction. Like you had a compass in the back of your head. I can bump into trouble enough without getting lost. I get floggings enough as it is."

"You two yonder! Thompson and McPherson!" they heard old Bones bellow from the house door. "On the double. I'm to parade you before the headmaster."

"Now what?" Sam rumbled as, in their ill-fitting, coarse gray coats and tight knee breeches they jogged toward the huge brass knocker, gleaming warm and friendly through the murk. Shouldering open the heavy oak door, they all but collided with old Bones.

"Steady all, or I'll lay ye by the ears," Bones growled. Having lost a leg fighting in the Americas, he had been in constant ill-humor since last September, when George the Third had signed his humiliating peace with the colonists. In fact, he seemed to have taken this as a personal affront and to consider himself shabbily done by for his services in the war. But then the present monarch was unpopular everywhere and such grumbling about his rule—or lack of it—found many echoes among the average people.

"What's up, Bones?" David asked. His reaction was direct as always, for he had little patience with guesswork, in class or out of it. Perhaps this was why he excelled in algebra, mechanics and his elementary navigation. Perhaps, too, his insistence on knowing, and being taught, the clear-cut truth was what had placed him in the bad books of several of the masters. These, with little real interest in their subjects, and even less in the charity boys they were supposed to teach, put him down as a troublemaker.

16

Bones shook his head and, with the two of them in tow, stumped along the passage. Halting them before the head-master's door, he eyed them severely. Bones was all for discipline, but though McPherson seemed suitably awed, his companion steadfastly returned the old servitor's look.

"Cocky young rascal, ain't ye?" he commented sourly but with a hint of admiration. He kept glaring down at the short, sturdily-built young figure whose ruddy face, snub nose and black hair, cut straight and low across his forehead, gave him an odd, even impish look. Then, with a grunt, he rapped with his staff on the door of the Head's chambers and paraded the two boys inside.

David could count on the fingers of one hand the times he had been summoned before the headmaster. Clearest of all was the memory of the day when kindly Abram Acworth had brought him here to appeal for his admission as a charity boy. That was soon after his father's death, when his mother had been at her wit's end to find bread for her little family. The son of a poor weaver who had been buried in the potters' field was not the sort to have influential friends, and as his mother's only support, David had known years of desperate poverty before Master Acworth had befriended him.

"Square those shoulders and speak when you're spoken to, not before," Bones warned as he respectfully withdrew.

Though it was still early afternoon, no light came through the casements, and the figure in wig and gown behind the massive table seemed more formidable than ever. Pushing aside his quills and inkpot, he spread a crackling parchment before him, its weighty seals red in the candle light.

"This is a request from the Honourable Company of Gentlemen Adventurers of England Trading into Hudson's Bay." He took a pinch of snuff, tweaked his nose and eyed the pair to make sure they were duly awed by mention of so famous a name.

17

"These gentlemen require four boys," he went on. "Boys who have had sound training in the elements of navigation are not to be found on every street corner and I esteem it high honor their request has come to this school. They wish four Gray Coat boys to be apprenticed for seven years at their posts in America."

David could feel his heart thumping beneath his heavy coat. The headmaster continued:

"Through ill fortune of various kinds, the school can supply but two." He fingered his snuff box a moment. "I have been pleased to submit the names of David Thompson and Samuel McPherson to the company."

Even then, David felt a passing curiosity at how Sam was taking it. As charity boys, they could expect to have little choice in such matters, but to have their futures, perhaps their entire lives, decided for them in so arbitrary a fashion would certainly not be to Sam's liking. And David himself felt that a question or two would be in order.

But the headmaster thought otherwise. "I'm through with them, Bones," he called. "You may take them out."

Bones entered promptly, saluted, then marched the two boys out of the room and back along the passage.

"What's it like yonder, across the water?" David asked excitedly.

"You'll find out, right soon," Bones snapped. "And I'll have two less to plague me."

"Come on now, Bones," David urged. "I want to know."

The old soldier glanced down at the eager face. Thompson had a direct, intense way with him which Bones, when he first arrived at the school, had mistaken for rudeness. But, old campaigner that he was, he had come to believe that wherever the fortunes of life took the boy, he would be one of those rare ones who win through—or who, if they fail, do so in no ordinary way.

18

"It's a rugged and bitter land," Bones said. "So cold in winter, my lads, that the trees crack and the frozen lakes and rivers boom out like cannon fire. There's wild beasts a-plenty, and half-naked savages who'll snatch yer scalps as quick as a wink."

"You must have liked it some, though," David persisted. "You were angry when the king surrendered it."

Bones chewed his scraggy mustache. "There's that about it, lads, I can't find words for. So big and wild it is, not like England. Times I was afeard and hated it. But it has a brave freedom, too, for a man with the heart to take it. Aye," he said with an odd wistfulness, " 'tis a new world and a man can be his own master there. Times, I wish I'd stayed. But, there, I've made my bed, now I must lie in it, so what's the use of talking?" He shot Sam a glance. "And you? What have you to say about all this?"

"What do you expect me to say?" Sam asked sullenly. "You heard him. We're given no choice. It's been decided for us."

"You're not lords' sons," Bones reminded him, "with the chance to pick and choose. So you'd as lief stay in Merry England?" he added, giving the name ironic emphasis.

All too well David knew what he meant by that. "Merry England" it might be for the rich and the nobility, but for the poor, brutalizing poverty was the common lot. The oft-expressed belief that "to educate the people is no business of government" still prevailed in high places. "If we teach the working classes to read and write," those in positions of privilege argued publicly, "we are writing our own death warrant. Even now opportunity is none too plentiful but if we are to teach the sons—to say nothing of the daughters— of every yokel and day laborer, then those of gentle birth will have a sorry time of it. What then, pray, will happen to our fortunes?"

19

Nor was the manner in which many of these fortunes were made considered any concern of the government. There was as yet no impassioned Charles Dickens to remind the selfish and high-placed that "mankind is your business." The lowly were taught "to be content with that estate to which God has called you." Gambling was rife, fortunes were being made in the slave trade and the liquor traffic offered sodden forgetfulness of their misery to male and female, old and young alike. Gin shops gave "drunkenness for one penny, dead-drunkenness for tu'pence with free straw to lie on." The penalty for petty theft was death, the law demanded the execution of female criminals by burning, and convicts were sold into the colonies for twenty pounds, there to slave for the remainder of their lives.

Yet beneath the surface of this appalling society, a new spirit was stirring. Ten years before, John Howard had begun his crusade for prison reform. And in Wales, as in the north and west of England, Wesley and his derided "Methodists" were bringing to the poor a sense of worth. Robert Raikes of Bristol, father of the Sunday School, was championing both religious and day school education.

Here in England, David Thompson was aware of the injustices and handicaps confronting him. He saw ignorance for what it was—a prison. And stirred by old Bones' "a man can be his own master there" he saw in the New World, in spite of isolation, danger and privation, his only chance of freedom and equal opportunity.

CHAPTER THREE

THE NORTHEASTER continued
and the *Prince Rupert* made heavy weather of it up the east
coast. Besides being heavily laden with trade goods and the
multitude of supplies needed in the posts whose only access
to the outside world was by the company's yearly ships, she
was strongly sheathed and timbered against the ice. The
stanchions and crossbeams below deck made proper stowage
difficult, and it was soon evident that, once they hove to in
the Orkneys to await the other two company ships making
up the convoy, the hatches must come off and all cargo be
secured before the northern crossing began.

For two days Sam lay inert in the bunk. There were times when David bent over him, watching and listening with mounting anxiety for any indication that his former school-mate still breathed. Now and then one of the sailors would come in and go away, shaking his head. The master neither appeared nor seemed to care, one way or the other. However, Mr. Summers, the first officer, visited the cuddy several times and took it upon himself to see that a blanket was provided from the ship's stores.

"By the cut of his jib, I'd say he was a new hand, still green in the smuggling trade," he commented one afternoon. "I've no doubt whatever it was him I saw go overboard. But whether he was flung overside for dead, or whether he jumped because he preferred drowning to what was in store for him, is anybody's guess."

"If he should come to, what will happen to him, sir?" Dave asked, making it sound as impersonal as he was able. "Will he have to stand trial?"

Mr. Summers shrugged. "That's for the master to decide. If he lives, it will go hard with him, no matter what." With his hands behind his back, he stood looking thoughtfully down at the figure in the bunk. "In his place, I'd about as soon be dead. For should the master put him ashore to shift for himself, he'll be a fugitive to the end of his days. And with that telltale disfigurement, wherever he goes he'll be a marked man."

As the long hours passed, David scarcely left the cuddy. If Sam should rouse while Jem was present and give the slightest indication of recognition, David believed that in itself would finish things for the charity boy. To be picked up at sea, even from a smuggler, was one thing. But to be a deserter from the company's service and have that fact dis-covered aboard one of the company's ships was a hundred times worse, for then the master would be in duty bound to turn Sam over for the law to take its course.

"If only I knew what happened aboard the smuggler," David kept thinking. "If Sam had mutinied or resisted, it might at least keep him out of Execution Dock." Not, of course, that the high and mighty officers of the company would make any allowances for that. A deserter who had broken his bond would be given short shrift, no matter what. But it might ease Sam's sentence somewhat if he had stood up to the smugglers, no matter how belatedly. And with his wound to prove it—

A low, tremulous moan came from the bunk. Sam was stirring. David reached for the pannikin of water he had kept ready on the locker and held it to the other's lips. Their eyes met and behind the dullness and confusion in Sam's there came dawning recognition.

David darted to the door and bolted it. "Never let on you know me," he urged in a low, tense voice. "I'll explain when you're stronger. But right now your life's at stake."

Tears of weakness and regret started in Sam's bewildered eyes. "When it was too late, I tried to get out of it. Honest I did."

"Not now," David pleaded. "And remember—"

"I—I must have been out of my head to go at all," Sam insisted on saying. "They—they talked me into it. I wanted to get even." He groaned, not so much from pain, David imagined, as from the anguish of contrition. "There at the last I said we should surrender. And when they wouldn't I—I sort of made a grab. I tried to slack the halliard then—" Fumblingly he touched his head.

So it was a cutlass wound! And that fluttering at the peak of the after sail told how close poor Sam had been to forcing the smugglers to surrender before they cut him down.

Utterly weak and all hope gone, Sam began to blubber. "And now I'll swing for it."

"You will if you don't keep your mouth shut," David warned him. "You're aboard the *Rupert,* understand? If the master so much as suspects you're the Gray Coat boy who skipped out on the company, he'll turn you over, sure as shooting."

Sam made a feeble, floundering attempt to sit up. Footsteps were approaching. It might be Jem, or Mr. Summers—any of them. In desperation, David seized Sam's shoulders and forced him to lie down. "You don't know me. I don't know you. Get that into your head—and keep it there. If you forget, make one slip, your goose is cooked—"

The footfalls were almost at the door. David sprang toward the bolt and slipped it free. But whoever it was kept on past the cuddy toward the bow. David experienced a vast sense of relief. He knew he was no hand at covering up, at saying one thing and meaning another. Even in the half-light, Jem would probably have read his secret in his face. But secret it must stay, now and forever, if Sam McPherson were to have a chance to live, even if only to pay for his mistake.

Giving the rocky Scottish coast a wide berth, the *Prince Rupert* sailed on and in due time opened up Portland Firth. The three weeks she lay in Stromness were anxious ones for David Thompson. Fortunately for Sam's chances, the great amount of blood he had lost, added to severe exposure, made for a slow recovery. Then, too, the strict rationing of ship's biscuit and "salt horse" aboard the *Rupert* proved meager fare for a convalescent. So it was that for the greater part of the ship's stay in harbor Sam was unable to appear on deck. It was a case of "out of sight out of mind."

Not that the master would have forgotten him. "But the

24

old man has his worries," Jem said, "and out of sight is out of mind, most times."

There were occasions when David wished he were free to reveal to Jem the truth about the sick youth who shared their cabin. Jem was honest and friendly but, if he knew the facts about Sam, he would either have to unburden himself to the master or share in the concealment. And it was characteristic of David Thompson that, if blame there should be, he intended to shoulder it alone.

Actually, his conscience was free about the matter. Sam had never been given any choice in enlisting in the company's service, and the law of those days was so often harsh and vengeful, and the poor were at the mercy of the whims of those who administered it. Sam would have to pay for his mistake, in any case, but in the New World he could at least win another chance.

After long thought, this was the conclusion David had arrived at. Sam McPherson must be given the chance to make a fresh start overseas. There was nothing on this side of the ocean for ones like him. Here for the rest of his life he would have to be a fugitive, going from bad to worse. But in America all might well be different.

David saw how desperate living conditions were on these island outposts of Europe. On this treeless, stormswept patch of earth, people were worse off than amid the direst poverty in London. While the crew made the needful changes below deck and while they waited for the two other vessels to appear, David had ample time to go ashore. A few sheep, fishing, and hard-won garden patches between the rocks were all the people had to provide food and clothing. Some of the islanders earned a few pence by gathering and burning the seaweed washed ashore by storms.

"They get some chemicals or other from the ash," Jem explained one evening as he and David leaned on the rail and watched the black and bitter smoke swirling down-wind from the furnaces across the anchorage. "No wonder the company can recruit so many able-bodied men here for their service overseas. Much as I'm against spending my life in the wilderness, I'd take it any time to trying to make a living here." Jem stared across the water at the bare and cheerless land. "Lucky for our shipmate in the cuddy yonder he's still too groggy to be put ashore."

"What do you suppose the master will do with him?" David asked.

Jem considered. "Mr. Summers thinks the old man'll bide his time. Then one fine day when we're lying at Churchill or York Factory he'll scare the daylights out of him and tell him to take his choice."

"His choice of what?"

"Of staying at one of the forts, doing menial labor to work out his passage—or coming back in irons to face the music. The company's in desperate need of workmen, and the old man holds the whip hand. He's nobody's fool, you know. And it'll be a feather in his cap with our gentlemen in London, him providing the post with a servant—no wages paid and no questions asked."

Pondering this possibility, David was relieved when at last the two companion ships appeared. A few days later, with all cargo trimmed and hatches battened down, the *Prince Rupert* signaled she was ready to proceed and the hazardous voyage began.

For weeks the wind held fair. Several times they sighted whalers homeward bound to Scotland and Norway from the Polar seas. As the ship's company fell into the routine of the long voyage, David came to understand the attraction which life at sea holds for those who follow it. By now Sam was strong enough to get about the deck in fair weather. Seemingly his grim experience aboard the smuggler and his narrow escape from drowning had not dampened his liking for a seafarer's life, and he showed increasing interest in the working of the ship.

"What's the master going to do with me?" he speculated gloomily when Jem was on watch and they were alone.

Remembering Sam's fear of the wilderness, David hesitated to tell him Jem's views on the matter. But, still and all, considering the alternative, it should make Sam easier in his mind to know.

Sam sucked in his lips and gave David a long, calculating look. It was a week now since the bandage had been taken off. A lumpy, gleaming scar ran from his ear partway across his cheek almost to the bridge of his nose. Some muscle or nerve on that side of his face must have been injured by the cutlass for it seemed incapable as yet of any expression other than one of stiff attention, of wry and rigid watchfulness. Even when Sam attempted one of his rare smiles, his face took on a look of twisted mockery. "Is that his idea—or yours?" he wanted to know.

"I'm only telling you what Jem told me."

"Things are turning out the way you wanted, aren't they?" Sam asked pointedly.

David, puzzled, asked what he meant by that. It was absurd, and no doubt the contracted muscles of Sam's face had something to do with it, but David was left with an uneasy feeling that Sam was taunting him, accusing him.

"I can look out for myself, don't you forget," Sam said, evading the question.

"Did I say you couldn't?"

Sam turned, took a step or two toward the cuddy, then came back. "You've not told them who I am? That we know each other?" And when David shook his head Sam seemed satisfied—more satisfied than David had at that time any way of knowing.

27

Each noon when Mr. Summers or the master stood on the poop and took observations, David thought how wonderful it must be to set the courses and keep the *Prince Rupert* headed unerringly toward her destination. After he reached the Bay and began the survey and navigation work for which he had been articled, he too would gain more knowledge and experience. Perhaps seven years from now, when he was fully qualified and was returning for his first leave, they might invite him to the poop where, as man to man, they would compare notes and discuss their chosen craft.

One noon, when Mr. Summers looked down and saw Dave watching him while he shot the sun, he lowered his sextant and glared with pretended severity. "You've been doing that for days," he called down. "Curiosity killed the cat, y'know." Then, with a chuckle, he beckoned David to join him on the poop.

"You seem to take a lively interest in nautical reckoning, Thompson," Mr. Summers said when David joined him. "Do they teach you Gray Coats that, as well as the knack of getting into mischief?"

At the words "you Gray Coats," a chill seemed to run up and down David's spine. Had Mr. Summers guessed Sam's secret then? "A bit of both, sir," David answered, and wondered what was coming.

"I can well believe the mischief part of it," Mr. Summers said. "But, here, take this and let's see what sort of fist you make of it. Careful now." And with that he placed his sextant in David's hands.

Telling himself there was no untoward significance behind Mr. Summers' mention of the school, David braced himself to the ship's roll as he had watched the officers do, raised the brass instrument to his eye and sighted the sun, then took the reading as he had been taught.

"Not bad, not bad at all," the officer commented when he

28

had checked the reading. "I see you've had a squint or two through one of these before."

"A few times, sir." Then, after asking how far David had advanced in his studies, and learning the branch of work he was being assigned to, Mr. Summers completed his observation, logged it and invited David down to his cabin.

"You're fortunate to be assigned to Churchill," Mr. Summers told him when they had settled themselves below. "There you'll be serving under the most celebrated land geographer of our times. You've read of Samuel Hearne?"

David had to admit that he had not.

"Then you've a treat in store for you. Rise up a moment." Opening his sea chest, Mr. Summers took out a book. "Written by the great man himself, *A Journey to the North,* his own first-hand account of how he traced the fabulous Coppermine River to its mouth in the Arctic Sea. Would you like to borrow it?"

David was delighted. The Hudson's Bay country and all beyond were an unknown world to all but a few Admiralty surveyors and high officials of the great company. Now, by rare good fortune, he had in his hands a book on which he could feast his curiosity for days.

During that week David reveled in the imaginative and smoothly written account of Samuel Hearne's explorations. Because of it, he was almost able to forget Sam's aloofness and that peculiar remark of his. He studied the sketch maps of the great man's journeyings, shared his misfortunes with what he asserted were fainthearted or bungling native guides, deplored with the writer the failures of his first summer, and fairly squirmed with satisfaction as he devoured the chapters dealing with the explorer's eventual triumph. And as he closed the book, David Thompson thought how exceedingly lucky he was to begin his life in the New World under so illustrious a navigator.

CHAPTER FOUR

T<small>HE</small> *Prince Rupert* was south and considerably west of Greenland, so Mr. Summers told David, when, after weeks of exceptionally favorable weather, the fog closed in.

"This has done it proper," Jem said disgustedly. "There'll be ice ahead and it'll be double watches till we clear the bergs." The two of them were in the cuddy, munching their breakfast of salt beef and hard biscuit. "Our friend will be getting his sailoring with a vengeance."

David nodded thoughtfully. The master had ordered that, now Sam was fit again, he should work his passage. But this proved to be one order Sam obeyed without grumbling. A week before he had moved into the ordinary seamen's quarters and though they were not thrown together as formerly, David saw enough of him to know that Sam was accepting his duties with a will. "I've long wanted to be a seaman," Sam had told him as they met on deck. "Funny, isn't it, I had to go through all this to get my chance?" He gave his old schoolmate one of his rare grins. "If I can prove to the bosun I'm worth my salt, he may keep me on the ship's company."

"You mean you'll ask to make the return voyage?" Dave asked anxiously. "They'll be on the lookout in London for you. Suppose they recognize you and—".

With a sour attempt at humor, Sam winked and pointed at his scar. "My own mother wouldn't be able to do that. It's an ill wind—" Sam let his distorted grin finish the sentence and, with a swagger new to him, turned to his work.

Thinking it over later, David realized there was a good deal of sense to what Sam had said. "Why, Geordie or old Bones could run smack into him and never know," he told himself. "He'll never be the kind who'll take to wilderness life." And certainly this last week Sam had displayed more spirit and initiative than David would ever have thought him capable of. This odd twist of fate had given him a purpose and an objective which could make a different person of him. "And with what he already knows of navigation stowed away in the back of his head—"

Warily, day after day and often out of sight of one another, the three ships held their course through those dangerous waters. Once, half-seen and ghostly through the fog, a towering iceberg loomed close abeam. The breakers along its ice cliffs and deep in its green caverns echoed across the water with a long-drawn-out moan of desolation, boding ill for any vessel whose lookout failed to be on the alert.

But, fortunately, during the time the fog hampered them, the bergs and floes were comparatively few. Only when at last the sun broke through and the fog dispersed did David realize how widespread the danger was. One morning when a light but steady wind had cleared the air, David was puzzled by a strange brightness over the horizon dead ahead.

"The ice blink," Jem explained. "Sunlight on the ice. There's floes ahead, worse luck."

Later, when they had stowed their pannikins, Jem proposed they climb to the foretop. "That's the place to see it from. It's quite a sight."

When they went aloft, there was nothing exceptional to see, but gradually the masses of ice came into view. At a distance it looked as though there were a solid barrier from north to south with no way for the ships to get through. But as they sailed nearer, open leads began to appear, and what had seemed at first to be merely hummocks took on height and color—bergs blindingly white where the sun struck the ice cliffs, blue-green and mysterious where the shadows seemed to crouch like gigantic, prehistoric monsters.

After Jem went on watch, David climbed down and joined the lookout in the bow. The shimmer of sunlight gave the very air a magical quality. On either side of the open leads the ship threaded there was ice as far as the eye could see, and David asked himself what would happen if a shift of wind closed the ice around them.

Jem, coming forward to perform some duty, paused a moment. "It minds me of the Arctic as Samuel Hearne writes of it," Dave told him.

Jem grinned. "You lay great store by that book, don't you?"

"And why not? It's a marvel of a book. When I had my nose in it I felt I was right there, sharing the adventure of the brave man who wrote it."

"Adventurer, right enough," Jem replied. "Brave, too, for all I know. Though there's them who don't think so," he added meaningly.

"So? Well, I know Mr. Summers isn't one of them," David defended his hero. "You should hear him talk about Samuel Hearne."

"Every man has a right to his opinion. Seems you've not heard how we lost Fort Prince of Wales. Or have you?"

David had to admit he did not even know there was such a place.

"You will, before you've been many weeks in the Bay." Just then the boatswain's whistle sounded in the waist and Jem turned to go. "It makes a cowardly story."

Samuel Hearne a coward? The very first chance, he would get the rights of this from Mr. Summers, David decided. But he had no opportunity to do so that day, and during the anxious days and nights which followed, David knew better than invade the poop.

Conditions worsened steadily. There seemed no end to the ice, and several times only the sharp eyes of the lookouts and smart handling of the ship saved all hands from disaster. Sam, steadied by the responsibility, proved himself no shirker and while he seemed to hold himself aloof from the men of the crew, he did his work well and brought down on his head none of the tongue lashings given by the master to some of the other hands.

It took a weary month before the convoy worked its way through the ice and into Hudson's Straits. Then, well inside the bay, the three ships parted company.

"One is bound for the posts at the Moose and Albany Rivers and the other puts in at York Factory. We're for Churchill, the most dismal of the lot," Jem explained.

Soon the *Prince Rupert* sighted the granite coast and followed it southward until the mouth of the Churchill River

33

was reached. Here, on a low point of rock and sand, David saw what looked like stone battlements. "Is that some ruined fort?" he asked.

"Fort it was. And could be still," one of the seamen told him, "only for the white-livered Hearne."

"What had he to do with it?"

"Do with it?" the old salt snorted. "He surrendered it to the French two years ago, without so much as a show of fighting. Fort Prince o' Wales we called it then. An' we were proud of it. So strong and well laid out it could have kept an army at bay."

"Master Hearne did some brave things in the Arctic," Dave protested warmly.

"Did he now?" the sailor retorted. He spat overside and stumped away.

For the score or so of white men at Churchill, the arrival of the *Prince Rupert* was the big event of the year. For David Thompson it was vastly more than that. What little carefree boyhood he had known was behind him now. In this wild country, he must play a man's part henceforth. Until now, his mounting anticipation had given a certain sense of unreality to these last weeks. A new life awaited him, but because it lay in the future, he could shape it in imagination to suit himself; he could pass by the hardship, privation and isolation, and dwell on the adventure and excitement, creating and discarding, to build a thrilling prospect for himself.

But from the time the ship entered the river mouth, a feeling of maturity, a press of necessity, stern and inescapable as the land itself, came to him. *This* was his future, a dream no longer, but a future which was *now*. In this inhospitable land men succeeded and failed, fought and died, fumbled and paid with their lives for one neglect or one mistake. Standing

34

in the forepeak, with the tang of the spruce forests in his nostrils and the curving river unfolding before his eager eyes, old Bones' words came to him: "But it has a brave freedom, too, for a man with the heart to take it." Whether or not he had that heart, he dare not say. What he did know was that his time of testing was upon him and there could be no escape, no turning back.

After the ship had rounded the point, the last puff of wind had failed, and with the strong current of the river to contend with, pinnace and gig were manned, the hawser payed out, and the ship towed laboriously against the stream. Looking down at the brown water rippling against the vessel's sheer, David smiled at himself for ever thinking the Thames a mighty river. In what strange and trackless heart-land did this broad stream gather its untamed flow, and had human eyes ever looked on its source? It was stirring to see land so near after months away from it. And what a land it was! No trim fields or hedgerows, no kindly spires to show that man had conquered, no green meadows with their winding, spiritless streams. Only unbroken miles of spruce and larch and willow, and in the endless distance the low, blue contours of the hills.

A sense of space so vast it dwarfed the human spirit made itself felt. And what deep and timeless silence! The small noises of the ship, footfalls on deck, the blocks complaining in the now-slack rigging, stressed the immense hush brooding over all. And this was but the outermost fringe; to adventurers such as Samuel Hearne it would be homey and familiar. What must it be like in the unmapped reaches to the west and north?

Beyond the toiling sailors in the boats ahead, David could see where the estuary ended and the low banks marked the river proper. In the waist, the ship's carpenter, with Sam helping him, was at work getting the covers off the battened hatches. Then, at last, toward evening, the *Prince Rupert* cleared a bend in the channel, and on the gently sloping shore ahead David saw the log stockades and the buildings of Fort Churchill.

Immediately the anchors were down, the master, with his dispatch box under his arm, stepped into the gig.

Just then Jem came scrambling down the mainmast shrouds after lending a hand at the clewing-up. He pointed shoreward. "There's your Governor Hearne. Him in the scarlet coat."

David stared at the gentleman who stood on the low cutbank, his hand on his sword hilt, waiting to greet the master. In his ruffles, tunic and sword, pistols in his belt and with a jaunty, plumed hat, he looked a brave figure. "A proper cavalier," David thought. Well, he would learn soon enough what manner of man Samuel Hearne was. It was characteristic of David Thompson and of his straight, unprejudiced manner of thinking, that he intended to begin his service here with no bias or hastily-made opinions either way. Facts were facts and would speak for themselves in due time.

This determination to form no false judgment of the man was put to the test a short while later. The longboat had been loaded gunwale high with the first of the stores and was about to push off when Mr. Summers motioned for David to get aboard. He scrambled over the rail and when he had perched himself atop the load he chanced to look up and see Sam standing there. Their eyes met and held for an instant, and he knew that Sam, too, was wondering if this would be their good-bye. But no word must pass between them if Sam's uneasy secret was to be kept. The sailors began sculling the boat toward land.

When David stepped ashore, the Governor, standing with two gentlemen David learned later were the surgeon and the deputy governor, beckoned imperiously.

"And who, may I ask, are you?" Governor Hearne inquired when David stood before him, hat in hand. "Unless our gentlemen in London are playing some prank on me, you're not by any chance my new apprentice?"

"I am, sir," Dave told him.

The Governor smiled, but there was mockery, and irritation too, in the smile. "I ask for a navigator and you see what they send me—a beardless boy!" he exclaimed to the two others. "And filled no doubt with brave dreams of winning fame and fortune in the New World." Then, seriously, to David, "But where are the three others who were to come with you? The three I asked for?"

David did not know how to answer. If the Governor ever learned that out there in the ship, and disguised beyond recognition by that hideous scar, was one who had broken his bond with the company! If, here and now, he asked some question David could not evade—! Then young Thompson's heart seemed to skip a beat as he saw the master had overheard and was turning to explain.

"I think, Governor, all that is explained for you in the dispatches. From the little I saw of this one during the voyage, he seems a likely sort. Or at least he's not spirit-broken like some of these charity lads."

"I shall soon be in a position to judge of that," the Governor answered. He beckoned a half-breed servant and gave him some order in the native tongue. "Now, Thompson, off with you. And when this fellow has shown you your quarters, nip back here. There's work to do, and not hands enough to do it."

A great feeling of relief came over David as he shouldered his bundle and hurried after the servant. It had not been an encouraging beginning. Keeping his own counsel about poor Sam was one thing. Lying to shield him was quite another. And it was certain now that the master suspected nothing as to Sam's identity. The Governor's words and haughty manner did nothing to make a strange boy feel at ease but no doubt

37

he had many more important things to think about than a green apprentice.

The press of work during those next days allowed Dave very little time to reflect on Sam McPherson and his troubles. It was as yet only early September, but in these latitudes the nights were noticeably closing in. As long as daylight served, and afterward under the flare of pitch-pine torches, the unloading went on. Besides all the provisions and trade goods, an astounding number of casks were brought out of the hold and carried on men's backs to the storehouse, which David was surprised to find not completed or secure against the winter.

All the buildings, with the noticeable exception of the Governor's private dwelling, were in much the same state. The stockade, however, had been strongly built and reinforced and, if properly manned, should be able to repel attack either by the marauding French or raiding savages.

These Indians, though, did not seem to be troublemakers. Their lack of spirit surprised David. Back and forth, from boat to storehouse, they carried prodigious loads on their sweating backs, and he marveled that their squat bodies did not crumple under such loads. The women worked as hard as their men and some of them made trip after trip with three hundred pounds on their backs. Bowed under such burdens, they made David think of gnomes. The glare of the torches and the broad leather bands across their foreheads, in the loop of which the loads were slung, increased this odd illusion.

When the last of the cargo had been brought ashore, the year's hoard of furs was sent aboard: bales of beaver, pine marten, mink, ermine, muskrats and other lesser pelts, each compactly shaped in the great fur presses and securely bound for stowage, and all destined for the world of fashion in England and on the continent. From what he had learned from *A Journey to the North*, and by the pitiable garb of the Indians here, it seemed to David that warm furs would be of more service among these native people than adorning the backs of elegant ladies and gentlemen at home.

David had been assigned to help the kindly deputy governor check the bales and make preliminary tallies for the official invoices. The day of departure was near and between long spells on duty he found time to pen a letter to his mother.

Jem had offered to deliver it in person. "And, remember," David cautioned when he handed it over to the young seaman, "no word to her about your opinion of the Governor."

Jem nodded. "Maybe it was just talk—fo'c'sle scuttle-butt. Too bad I mentioned it, seeing as how you can't do a thing about it, no matter what sort of man he is. I'll give your mother only hopeful news of you."

"I've written her I'm soon to continue my training in navigation under one of the most famous navigators."

"Let's hope so." After he had tucked the letter inside his jacket, Jem went on, as if it were an afterthought: "Our castaway's to be left here. Or had you heard?"

David looked up sharply.

"It's the truth. The Governor is so put out with the failure to supply him with the apprentices he was promised—and any other kind of European labor, skilled or otherwise, for that matter—that the master's turning this fellow over to him. Poor devil, it isn't much of a prospect, is it?"

This was grim news indeed for David. And not only because of his concern for the unfortunate boy. Sam hated and feared isolation. Had he been left to follow the sea, he could have made a place for himself. But here, thrown together, and with the secret which must be guarded at all costs—

"Has he been told yet?" David asked. "How is he taking it?"

Jem shook his head. "He's been told, right enough. But how he feels about it, well, I can't say. He's no hand for talking, or telling about himself. There's something queer about that one, Dave. He's been one of the crew all this time, but what's his name, or where he comes from, none of us knows. My guess is, there's more than just the smuggling he's running away from. I may be wrong—" Jem hesitated, then looked at David. "What say?"

David took a deep breath. All along, this evasion had smacked to him of double-dealing. Jem was as true and as square as an oak timber. Even yet he could squirm out of answering, David thought. But Jem could be trusted, and he was not going to lie to him, even by saying nothing.

"I knew him before—before this happened," David said forthrightly. "It would be better for your sake if you didn't know. But, Jem, if you want me to come out with it—"

"No. No, I don't," Jem interrupted. His expression softened. Suddenly he thrust out his hand. "Sometimes I wondered if there wasn't something between you two. And, look, I think all the more of you, Davvie. From the day I set eyes on you, I saw you were the sort who'd stick by a friend, no matter what. Whatever your secret is—and his—it's safe with me."

As the day of the *Prince Rupert's* departure neared, the press of work increased. More than ever, when they were able, Mr. Jefferson, the deputy governor, and Mr. Prince, the sloopmaster, sought the company of the ship's officers. For, faced with the isolation of the coming winter, they wished to glean the last crumbs of news from the outside world. The storehouse was now filled to the rafters. Food for their bodies was assured, but it was food for their minds they hungered for. Opinions on the troubled state of England, on the future of the colonists a thousand miles to the south, personal news, the gossip of London town—these and all else they had heard would be talked over and debated many times during the winter.

"The world wags without us, Thompson," Mr. Prince said

with a wry smile one evening. "Mark my words, we'll pump you dry with our questions before the winter's over. When a man's turn for home leave comes, he doesn't want to have lapsed into savagery through ignorance."

But in contrast to the fort people's reluctance to see the ship depart, the *Prince Rupert's* company was all impatience to be off. The mellow Indian summer had gone and at night, in the chill moonlight, the wild bugles of migrating geese warned that cold weather was at hand. Of them all, only Governor Hearne, with his debonair bearing and mocking smile, seemed indifferent to the departure. To David, it seemed that here was one man too resolute and dashing, too independent and resourceful, to know the pangs of homesickness. Here was one on whom the wilderness had set its seal, and whose face was toward the New World, not the Old, one who had accepted the challenge of the unlocked North.

CHAPTER FIVE

WHEN THE DAY of departure
came, David did his best to escape the feeling of many of
those left behind that they were exiles. He said his farewells
to Jem Little and Mr. Summers, then stood in silence with
the others who lined the beach. Sam, who had been assigned
the duties of the Governor's body servant, had been down
earlier, but as the boats pushed off Jem looked for him in vain.

"If it's Scar Face you're looking for, he went inside the
stockade some time back," a man called out.

David looked and, sure enough, there was Sam lounging

just inside the gate. "He daren't trust himself," David thought. "He wants people to think he doesn't care, one way or the other." Well, being Sam, that was natural enough. If only Sam had given him some hint as to how he was taking this arbitrary banishment! But not once since the master had turned Sam over to the Governor had he so much as spoken to him. And now, withdrawn, embittered, he had gone back to the fort as if to show his former crew mates that none of them meant anything to him.

As soon as the ship's gig had been hoisted aboard, the rough-voiced chantey of the homeward bound came from the seamen at the capstan bars. David watched the anchors broken out and catted. Then, towed by the longboat, the ship swung slowly into the current of the river. The company ashore fell strangely silent; then, as if drawn by some invisible cord, they moved along the bank, keeping abreast of the vessel until, with bunting flying and parting cheers from those aboard, it quickened with the river and passed them on the headland.

The whites of the fort's company had turned out in best attire that morning. Now, back in the uncompleted guard-house where he was quartered with others of the staff, Dave changed into his working clothes.

"Aye, that's right," the surgeon approved with forced heartiness. "No medicine like work, I always say. Makes a man forget his troubles." And opening his chest, he laid away his broadcloth coat and donned an old buckskin jacket.

The Governor apparently shared the surgeon's view on the benefits of work, for they had hardly turned out before he was in the square, shouting orders to all within the palisades. David was mustered, with ten or twelve native axemen, for wood-cutting fatigue. With Mr. Prince in charge, they manned the sloop and rowed a mile upriver to continue the seemingly endless task of cutting firewood and carrying it to the fort.

Standing at the tiller, Mr. Prince kept a course close inshore to take advantage of whatever back eddies there were. Had they kept to midstream, they might have glimpsed the *Prince Rupert's* spars, now miles away at the river mouth. But much as he wanted to, David did not allow himself a backward look.

"I don't suppose you've fired a gun in your life," Mr. Prince said. He tapped the fowling piece resting against the combing of the cockpit. "Well, you'll not learn sooner. No poulterer's shop at the corner here, y'know. When we see these fellows set to work, we'll walk overland to a spot I know and see what we can find."

By the time they reached the wooded island where the hewers were to work, the lingering chill of night had been dispelled and the sun lay so warmly on his back that David peeled off his jacket.

Mr. Prince nodded. "You'll find this the most pleasant season of the year. No mosquitoes."

"What's a mosquito?" David asked.

"The plague of this land, mosquitoes. It's them make the bitter winters endurable, for then's the only time they're not sucking our blood, the devils." Mr. Prince chuckled. "What's a mosquito? I'll not repeat that at the fort, so they'll not be making fun of you like they did another Gray Coat boy asked the same thing, years back."

"What was his name, sir?" David asked.

"Young Jack Jennings. He's senior apprentice now, at York Factory. You knew him?"

David nodded. "Though he'll not remember me. I was still in lower school when he left. Some of the boys asked me to find out what had become of him, but I clean forgot."

"He's hale and hearty, the last we heard. That was overland, by courier, some while back."

"There's another I knew better. Alf Robinson. He's more my age."

"Robinson, aye. I've heard of him, though we've never

44

met," the sloopmaster said. "He's done his service, so far, at York."

Leaving the sloop well moored under the cutbank, the hewers took up their tools and followed a trail through the willows to the slightly higher ground toward the center of the island where there were evergreens of moderate size. After the men had scattered and the woods sounded with their axe blows, Mr. Prince struck out northward, toward some marshy ponds. David's only experience in hunting had been ratting in the mews and along the wharves near London Bridge. As he followed his guide through what, to him, seemed a trackless wilderness, he experienced for the first time, the hunter's feeling of primitive alertness and suspense. He stepped warily and kept a sharp eye ahead for the slightest movement. The time was coming, he knew, when he would be hunting, not for sport, but for food.

Following Mr. Prince's example, he advanced in a stealthy, crouching walk until, glimpsing the shining surface of the pond through the all but leafless willows, the sloopmaster motioned him down, and from there to the water's edge they proceeded in a crawl.

"Wild geese! Hear 'em?" Mr. Prince whispered, indicating a small, reedy bay directly opposite. Ripples were coming from behind the screen of reeds and David could hear the low, throaty voices of the wildfowl as they fed contentedly and conversed with one another. "Keep low. They're sure to have a sentry."

Sure enough, guided by Mr. Prince's look, he saw a long, dark neck, motionless as a stick, reared above the long grass of a hummock. Shifting position ever so slightly, Dave brought it into outline against the darker woods behind until he could make out the white cheek patches of a guardian gander.

Suddenly the bird gave a guarded *"cro-onk!"* Instantly the splashing and feeding ceased.

45

"Confound it, he's discovered us!" Mr. Prince muttered. Through the reeds the entire flock were poised for flight. There was nothing for it but to crawl back behind the willows. "We'll never get within firing distance now—and my mouth is watering for roast goose for supper. This is a job we'll have to surrender to a native."

When they reached the clearing, Mr. Prince told two of the Indians what was wanted. They talked in their own language and then one of them jerked his head for a slight but well-set-up youth to come forward. Mr. Prince backtrailed and let the Indian examine the pond from behind the willow clumps. The Indian held out his hand and, after looking to his priming, Mr. Prince handed him the gun. "Do your best, Young Otter," he urged.

Young Otter took the weapon, walked back along the trail a few yards and slipped into the bushes so skillfully that not a twig tip stirred. Mr. Prince and David sat down to wait.

After what seemed to him a long time, David peered through the willows. The farther side of the pond was treeless for fifty yards from where the reeds ended and was bare of all cover except scattered grass clumps. The geese had resumed their feeding, with the sentry still in the same place. Here and there a gentle puff stirred the grass and ruffled the surface of the pond. Twenty minutes passed and David could see nothing to indicate that Young Otter had even left the willows. In any case, it seemed impossible that a fox, let alone a human, could approach within striking distance across such exposed ground.

And then the autumn stillness was torn apart by the explosion of the muzzle loader. The geese set up a clamor and rose steeply from the water, but where they had been feeding four bodies now floated. David saw Young Otter rise. It was unbelievable! The Indian had snaked to within twenty yards before firing.

46

It was a superb display of woodsmanship. "I still don't see how he could have come that close without them knowing," David declared. "How does he do it?"

"Don't ask me, lad! Neither of us could have done it—or ever will. Necessity's the best of teachers, and with these people it's succeed or starve."

David broke cover and raced to the edge of the pond to see Young Otter recovering the dead geese. "I'll learn to hunt like that," he resolved. "Some day I'll learn the secret." Standing erect in that quiet place, an odd feeling of inadequacy came over him. His first day away from the fort, and he had seen how little he really knew, how much he had to master—to handle a boat in the river current, swing an axe, stalk and shoot. Each day, each situation, would bring its particular challenge. There were no ifs and buts about this wilderness life, no excuses, and a partial success meant failure.

During those next weeks, hardly a day passed that David did not realize how much he could learn from these untutored people. Those whose duties kept them inside the fort might —and sometimes did—look down on them. "A pack of savages," Sam called them one day when, bungling a moccasin he was trying to patch, an old woman took it out of his hands with a tolerant yet somewhat derisive grin and did the job for him. David, fortunately, was handicapped by none of this white man's feeling of superiority. These people had lived for centuries in this hard land before the whites came to dispute its ownership, and their hard-won skill at wresting a living from the wilderness filled him with admiration. Words from a Gray Coat copybook came back to him: *A humble mind is the beginning of knowledge.* The color of a person's skin conferred no superiority, though there were those at the fort who thought it did. David knew that if ever he was to penetrate far into this wild country, this was a notion he could not

47

afford to entertain. There would be times when he too must "succeed or starve." He had always had a lively curiosity, and from that day on he set himself to learn all he could from the Indians.

"Never let an Indian think you don't know more than he does," he had heard a white man say. "Once you lose face with them, your command over them is finished." But in this untamed country, bluffing would not work. Knowledge was power, and he would gain that knowledge, even from the humblest.

Life at Fort Churchill soon settled into the routine of any other trading post. And here, besides the daily chores, there was much construction work still to be done. David pitched in with a will and was gratified to find that as the weeks passed he was learning a degree of axemanship from the half-breed and native workers. But, most of all, he kept looking forward to beginning his duties as navigator and surveyor. When would the Governor send for him? The heavy work in the keen air and the autumn sunshine brought physical satisfaction and each evening, after a long day with axe or paddle or hand-spike, he exulted in healthy physical weariness. His fair skin lost its London pallor and his muscles, unaccustomed at first to such frontier exertion, became hard and equal to the work.

But, as the surgeon put it: "Strong backs are a penny a dozen around a trading post. It's the lad with a head on him who gets ahead." But surely, David told himself, one of these days the Governor would send for him and put him through his paces. To prepare himself for this examination, he began brushing up on his mathematics in the evenings. At first it startled him to find how his penmanship had suffered because of the heavy manual work. Still and all, the new skills he had acquired should compensate for that, and after a few evenings he was pleased to see that his writing was improving.

The overcrowded, unfinished guardhouse where he was

quartered was a poor place to study. It was dark and, being built from green logs, became so chilly when the sun went down that his fingers became numbed. In the evenings and on Sundays, he began taking his books outside, sitting on the ground with his back against the log wall, and doing his exercises on his knees.

One Sunday morning, warming himself in the sunshine on the south wall of the guardhouse, he was leafing through the Bible which had been the headmaster's parting gift, while waiting for the surgeon to begin the morning services. His eyes came to a passage which had been a favorite of his father's:

"The earth is the Lord's and the fulness thereof: the world and they that dwell therein. For He hath founded it upon the seas and established it upon the floods."

David looked up as a shadow fell across the page. The Governor was regarding him with an enigmatic smile. "What's that you're reading, boy?"

David scrambled to his feet. "A psalm, sir. The twenty-fourth."

"So? Very pretty, I'm sure."

David did not know what to say. He had never thought of this majestic prose as "pretty." He did, however, accept it as true.

"I dare say they schooled you in and out of season on all things biblical—those Gray Coat masters of yours?

"Yes, sir."

"And did they teach you this? From St. Paul, if my memory serves me aright: *'When I became a man, I put away childish things.'* Now there's a passage to my liking. As for the rest of their pious nonsense, much good will it do you in this savage land." There was a tinge of derision in the Governor's tone, but his thin smile was not unfriendly. "By all means, read, my

49

boy. I've seen many an apprentice arrive here with an inquir-
ing mind, and I've watched them become dulled—rum-sodden,
some of them—placing no store in the delights of the intellect
—their own or their betters'. Being a student of human nature, it gives me a lively pleasure to observe their downfall.
They've none to blame but themselves. I'm bound to say,
however, that I'll be surprised if you let yourself go downhill
like that."

David was confused. This was the first time Samuel Hearne
had shown any interest in him personally. But there was con-
descension and raillery, too—

"By all means, read, improve your mind," the Governor
was saying, "but read the right things. Let me recommend to
you my favorite Voltaire and Hume, the atheist. Shrewd,
worldly men, the pair of them. Study their writings. Mark
them well. They'll knock your charity school teachings into
a cocked hat. You possess qualities all too rare in an apprentice, Thompson. You will go far here, once you learn to stand
on your own feet."

Stuffing his gauntleted hands inside his sword belt and
teetering on his heels, the Governor went on: "When I braved
the Arctic to map the Coppermine, Voltaire's *Dictionary* and
the *Nautical Almanac* were the two works I relied on." He
chuckled importantly. "They saw me through—they and my
own wits. Of course, if one is afraid of adventure, if one prefers to remain a sniveling clerk—"

Suddenly, seeing that his apprentice was neither awed nor
cowed, Hearne's manner changed abruptly. In those level eyes
looking up at him from below the square cut, black hair, he
saw more independence of mind than he had bargained for.
And contrary to all he had just said in favor of open-minded-
ness, having his opinions questioned was not to be tolerated
in a subordinate.

"Don't stand there gaping," he snapped. The condescending

banter was gone. His face flushed angrily and in that revealing instant he showed himself for what he was—a dictator. "What do you believe? Or have you lost your tongue?" he taunted.

"I see no reason to doubt what I have been taught—"

"A puppet, eh? And I fancied I saw in you the makings of a man of independent mind! I see I have deceived myself. But, then, in backwaters such as this, one who hungers for the rapier play of wit is prone to indulge his liking for the sport by trying it out on every clod. Go on with your stupid reading, boy. Far be it from me to dispel your pretty dream. And when the surgeon yonder gives the call for service, I dare say you will parrot the responses like the rest of them." And with this parting shot, the Governor tilted his plumed hat at an even more rakish angle and strutted off.

A few minutes later, the surgeon, having heard what was said from inside the guardhouse, came out. "He startled you, eh, lad? He doesn't like men who stick to their guns, and you're the first apprentice I've heard stand up to him like that."

"But he asked me what I believed! What else could I have answered?"

The surgeon laid a hand on David's shoulder. "The Governor is exceedingly vain in his opinions, and you've offended him. I'm sorry, for your sake, that this had to happen. He's one of those who can't brook opposition—a man who learns nothing and forgets nothing. With him, it's the toadies who get promotion."

The days shortened still more, and soon the long winter laid siege to the lonely, uncompleted fort. For week after week, Governor Hearne seemed not to know that an apprentice by the name of Thompson existed.

As David lay in his bunk alongside the green, poorly-

51

chinked logs, the moisture in them froze, and as the temperature dropped still lower, it seemed to him that the whole building was groaning and complaining beneath the cold's onslaught. Backwaters along the river were sealed in dark, glass-hard ice, and where the current ran strong it became dotted with the moving pan ice. Late that week the first snow rode in on a howling gale. The willows along the river were bowed with it, and drifted deep. It banked itself along the stockade and in the lee of buildings. The sky cleared and the sun appeared and at night the northern lights wheeled and danced. At times David imagined he heard the rumble of cannonading.

"It's the booming of the ice, setting deeper on every lake and pond," Mr. Prince explained.

On clear days, David and the junior officers were ordered to go out and shoot ptarmigan for food. Dave looked forward to these outings, for on stormy days they were condemned to pace the guardroom, wrapped in their beaver coats, to keep from freezing. By the Governor's orders, they were allowed only enough wood for one fire, night and morning.

The time came when David could stand this inactivity no longer. He asked for an interview with Mr. Jefferson, the deputy governor.

"I'll lose my penmanship and my schooling, too, for want of practice, sir," David told him.

Mr. Jefferson shrugged, making a helpless gesture with his hands. "I have my orders, Thompson, the same as the rest of you. What do you expect me to do?"

"I'd like to be set at the work I was apprenticed for."

Mr. Jefferson, knowing it was contrary to his superior's orders to discuss the conduct of affairs with juniors, did not answer immediately. Yet even his silence gave David to understand that Mr. Jefferson realized he had just grounds for protest.

"I'd help you if I could," the deputy said finally. "But we older ones, though in less degree, are in much the same straits as those in which you find yourself. As for writing paper, there is none, only a few sheets rationed out for official purposes. The Governor keeps the store of paper in his private quarters. And under lock and key at that."

The cold in the guardroom was so bitter that even as they talked, the pair had to keep walking. Hoar frost an inch thick covered the green, unpeeled logs. The Governor, wanting to have his own house snug, had not permitted time to chink these walls. Recently, in desperation, the staff had resorted to sousing the logs with water carried from the river, hoping that the ice so formed would at least keep out the wind and driving snow. Though none dared say so openly, all knew that the Governor was to blame for much of their present privation. And as he beat his hands together and stamped his feet to ward off numbness, the deputy, smarting under the injustice and mismanagement, spoke more bluntly than ever.

"Firewood, paper, the better cuts of what meat our hunters bring in—all go to provide comfort for one man, and one man only, hereabouts. Even if you could keep warm enough to write, scraps of birchbark are hardly the thing to do mathematic exercises on. You're quite right, my boy. A few more months of this and your schooling will pretty well have deserted you. I'd like to help you but, believe me, my hands are tied. Just the same, I'm going to speak on your behalf this afternoon. The Governor can call it interference if he likes." Then with a flash of anger: "Only for him we'd all be warm and secure in Fort Prince of Wales this winter!"

David recalled how, under the spell of *A Journey to the North,* he had refused to take any stock in what Jem had said. But like pieces of a puzzle, the surrender of the stone fort, Hearne's selfish regard for his own comfort here, the smoldering discontent with his dictatorial rule, all these were be-

53

ginning to form a picture of a vastly different man than his admirers in England knew. "What does he want with four apprentice surveyors when he won't use the one he has?" David asked himself. "I wouldn't believe all this talk; I said I'd be loyal to him, no matter what, but now—" And for the first time he allowed rebellious, helpless protest to have access to his mind.

The deputy would have unburdened himself still more but at that moment the surgeon, a jovial man with sandy side-whiskers, stamped into the room. "Laughs are few enough here," he burst out, "but come along if you want to see a sight to make a man forget his troubles. Bruin has broken into the Governor's private molasses barrel!"

David and Mr. Jefferson hurried outside. In the yard, immediately behind Mr. Hearne's house, the fort's half-tamed bear cub was sitting bolt upright in the snow. His face and forepaws were thickly plastered with the stiff, partly-frozen molasses and David saw Sam, beside himself with rage, dodging in and out, brandishing a broom, yet afraid to get close, in case the half-grown bear decided to attack. Sam darted to one side and then the other, but from whichever angle he advanced, the bear swung to face him. And, meanwhile, first with one paw and then with the other, it kept stuffing the molasses into its mouth and licking its chops with gusty satisfaction.

A dozen or so half-breeds and Indians had formed a ring around the pair and were laughing uproariously at poor Sam's expense. David had picked up enough of the native language to understand they were teasing the Governor's body servant for letting himself be outwitted by a bear. Looking over his shoulder, David saw the Governor standing in the doorway of his snug quarters. He, too, was laughing. But there was something in his laugh which made David's fists clench; a cruelty and a cold contempt and brittle, belittling mockery.

54

It made David think of old pictures he had seen, of medieval stories he had read—the lord in his castle, and his court jester in cap and bells, the facial muscles severed, as was done in the Middle Ages, to give the poor buffoon a twisted, mutilated grin. In a flash of intuition—and knowing now the callous egotism of the man—he sensed why Hearne had chosen Sam McPherson for his body servant. Poor, blundering Sam, not daring to defend himself from his master's cruel wit, even if he knew how! Derided, providing a target for Hearne's sarcastic humor, even his disfigurement a cause for inhuman merriment!

Mr. Jefferson nudged the outraged David. "The Governor seems in high good humor at the moment. I'm going to ask him about you here and now." For himself, David was in no mood to ask for favors from such a man.

The bear, much pleased with himself, had finally shuffled off and Sam had rolled away the damaged keg and was putting the timbers back into place across the Governor's store shed when Mr. Jefferson returned.

"You are to present yourself to him for work tomorrow," he reported, with more satisfaction than David was feeling at the moment.

Everyone else had returned to their quarters when David walked over to the shed. "You're all right?" he began. "The bear didn't—"

Suddenly Sam's hand shot out and he drew his former schoolmate into the narrow passage between shed and house. His face was twitching. "I've—I've had all I can stand of this!" he broke out, tortured by more emotion than Dave had ever seen him display. "You think I'm lucky, don't you? You think because I get the leavings of his fine food, and have a warm hole to sleep in above the rafters—" Sobs shook the beefy shoulders.

"Sam!" David urged. "Don't—I mean—"

"Isn't there some way I can break out of this torture-hole?" Sam pleaded. "Me—you? There'll be mutiny here yet. Can't we get away?"

"Away to where?"

"The woods—anywhere at all."

David shook his head. "Green ones like us, Sam? How long do you think we'd last, and in the dead of winter?"

Sam's slow nod admitted the hopelessness of any such plan. But walking back to the guardhouse, David Thompson promised himself that some day, somehow, there would be a way to better things. With a whole vast empire waiting to be mapped and explored, and he eager to do his full share in the task, his day would come. Had Governor Hearne, basking in the favor of the highly-placed in England, been able to read David's thoughts just then he would have had even more to laugh about.

CHAPTER SIX

David reported to the Governor as ordered. After the rigors of the guardhouse, the warmth and comfort of the big room made it hard to believe that within these palisades men were existing in buildings which a good farmer would not consider fit for his beasts. Firewood was not rationed here. All day and probably during the night as well, the fireplace was well supplied with logs. In front of the window, Governor Hearne would sit at his desk, reading and making leisurely notes. In the guardhouse, candles were not allowed, but here, when the light was dull, they burned all day.

David was provided with a bench and small table at the far end of the room, but there was no instruction. At odd times during the following weeks he was allowed to copy a few pages from the manuscript of *A Journey to the North*. How different it all sounded, now that he knew something of the man who had written it!

It was during the doubt and uncertainty of that first winter that David began recording his experiences and observations on scraps of paper discarded by the Governor, who used it lavishly, and often, with a show of impatience, would crumple a sheet on which only a few lines had been written and toss it onto the hearth for Sam to burn later. It was mainly with Sam's help that this paper was kept from being destroyed. On these pages David told of his disappointment at the pretense of clerical work assigned him. "At another time," he recorded, "I copied an invoice." Aside from this, there was little relief from the deadening idleness enforced on him while in the Governor's presence. However, Mr. Jefferson, Mr. Prince and the surgeon loaned him the few books in their possession. "Among them were several on history and animated nature," he wrote. "These I paid most attention to as the most instructive."

Instruction of any kind which would help him in his calling was what Dave wanted, and it was here that his growing friendship with Young Otter proved of benefit. Except when laboring for the company or when they came to trade, the Indians were not allowed inside the palisade. In his off hours, David began visiting the lodges of this young hunter and his people. Here, squatting around the fire, they began teaching him their language, and the way he joined in their laughter at his mistakes showed them that he was one white who could take a joke at his own expense.

Every new word they taught him he wrote in his diary. Before long he had several pages of these basic words and when he and Young Otter were sent to hunt together, Dave made it a rule that they should use only the Indian's native tongue. Snowshoeing through the near-by woods and marshes in search of small game or to visit their rabbit snares, David learned the language and much wood lore. Thus, by combining outings and instruction, he came to feel genuinely at home among these people with whom so much of his life was to be spent.

It was on these short excursions that he learned to read many of those wilderness messages and stories which are written on the snow. The wavering lines of crosses left by ptarmigan or partridge, the dotted tracks of questing foxes, and the network of rabbit runways became familiar to him. He knew the trails left by wolves and ermine, by wolverine and the shadow-loving lynx. Then one day, after a fresh snowfall, Young Otter, who was breaking trail, stepped aside and pointed.

"That rabbit scared." He grinned.

David examined the tracks. "How can you tell he's scared?"

Young Otter kept smiling and David looked again. "Now I see," he said. Instead of hopping in a straight line toward the next patch of timber, the tracks showed the rabbit had been leaping from side to side as it streaked for shelter.

Young Otter motioned for David to take the lead. Soon he saw that the leaps were becoming longer. But if some preying animal were chasing it, why should the rabbit lose ground by leaping from side to side? Then, at the end of one frantic leap which David paced as eighteen feet between footmarks, the climax was written in the snow. Two great wings had brushed the surface on either side of the last imprint. There was no sign of struggle, not even a drop of blood. The trail simply ended there. Beyond, the snow was unmarked.

"What bird you say killed him?" Young Otter questioned, brisk as any schoolmaster.

David thought hard. For one thing, he had learned that rabbits do not forage much before dusk. And, for another, he knew it had snowed last evening. Then, too, the wing tips had

59

left marks which were broader and less sloping than those a hawk would make. Also, there was a half-moon these nights, and Young Otter had taught him that the arctic hare loved to play in open places like this, or on lakes and beaver meadows, in the moonlight.

"You know?" Young Otter persisted.

"I say it was an owl—one of the great horned ones," David answered.

Young Otter looked at him steadily for a moment, then nodded his head with pleased satisfaction. "You are learning to use your eyes."

It was a compliment which David appreciated as much as if he had come through a stiff written examination with flying colors, for his young Indian teacher knew he had not guessed the answer. He had observed, used his eyes to gather every piece of evidence, and had taken advantage of his increasing knowledge of the ways of wild things. But what David Thompson learned most of all that day was that there was no magic in an Indian's understanding of nature's secrets. That was as logical as a problem in geometry. Straight thinking was as valuable here as in the classroom, but with this difference: in the classroom you got a second chance, but in the wilderness you paid with hunger, perhaps with your life, for wild guesses and errors in judgment.

If only the Governor were even half so conscientious a teacher, or if he even cared! But before long he told his apprentice that his presence in the house disturbed him and that he could not afford the time for "further instruction." Perhaps later, when he was not so busy—

Then and there, David knew he had nothing to hope for so long as he remained posted to Churchill. Sam was not the only one to realize he was trapped. Not a penny of wages for seven long years and his future, his very life, in the hands of this egoistic, callous man!

60

Yet this young native, who in the Governor's eyes was no better than a serf, gave freely of his time and hard-won knowledge, expecting nothing but friendship in return! And David's friendship he had, many, many times over. It was with enduring gratitude that the young apprentice turned to the Indian hearts and Indian lodges which were opened to him. In his writings, as in his dealings here, the Governor showed he considered Indians something less than human. But for David Thompson, then and to the end of his life, Indians were people, too.

CHAPTER SEVEN

Spring came at last to the Hudson's Bay country. After weeks of raw, blustery weather, the sun appeared, noticeably higher now and with a warmth which, at noon, thawed the ice from the south side of the guardhouse and left an ever-widening ribbon of bare ground at the base of the palisade. Snow buntings, jays and chickadees were seen and heard in increasing numbers. The gray and sodden ice moved out of the Churchill River, and that same night the sky echoed with the restless clamor of returning geese.

For David and those assigned to clerical duties, it was a busy time. Soon the Indian trappers would be coming down with their catches. Cases and bales of trade goods had to be opened and their contents tallied and laid out on the shelves of the trade room; hatchets, flintlock muskets, beads, mirrors, calico, kettles and a variety of other articles to catch the native fancy.

David knew this trade was the life blood of the company. He knew he must be proficient and display a consuming interest in it, and yet somehow it did not seem of first importance. Outside those drab walls, the wilderness was unfolding and its mystery and excitement pulled strongly. Although he had never penetrated it more than a day's travel from the fort, David was constantly aware of its challenge and allure. Freed of their snow, the low, rolling hills far upriver took on an inviting purple. Indians, waterfowl, even the small birds around the fort seemed infected with a glad sense of release. And here he was, vainly trying to keep his attention on the weighing of packets of salt and sugar and the displaying of trinkets in the low-beamed trade room! He knew then, with a tingling sense of finality, that he would never make his mark as a trader and that, thanks mainly to Young Otter's schooling, the wilderness had already set its seal on him.

Soon the first brigades of birchbark canoes arrived. All day and well into the night, David was kept on the jump behind the counter. He learned the rudiments of barter and of grading furs. Being city-born and knowing the trifling cost of most of the articles offered in exchange, he learned also of the childish ignorance of the Indians. Value and utility were of slight consideration in their eyes. The cheap, glittering novelties were what caught their fancy. For these they would pay out of all proportion to their value.

Out in the fur room, the great presses for baling the pelts of beaver, marten, mink and so on were in constant operation. More and ever more wigwams were pitched outside the palisade. At night the yelping of dogs, the crying of babies, and

63

sounds of the tom-toms and rattles of the medicine men were in sharp contrast to the winter's long silence. And still the canoes came. The riverbank held so many of them it seemed there was no room for one more to land.

With the coming of warm weather, other and less welcome visitors appeared. "Hudson's Bay is certainly a country Sinbad the Sailor never saw," David wrote in his makeshift diary, "as he makes no mention of Musketoes."

Through June and into July, trappers from far in the interior continued to arrive. David was struck by the contrast between these independent, self-reliant Indians and those who lived the year-round at the fort. Young Otter's family were for the most part a proud and vigorous lot, but the company hirelings, known as "packet Indians," were greatly inferior to these new arrivals.

"Most of these upriver natives will leave after the *Prince Rupert* arrives," Mr. Prince said. "It's the sight of her they're waiting for. But, then, the same could be said for the rest of us. A year's a long time without news of one's kith and kin."

"I'm hoping there'll be other news as well," David confided to him. "You told me Jack Jennings was transferred from here to York Factory. Down there he'll be given the chance to learn and get ahead. For myself, I've no hope of that here."

Sam McPherson, too, was pinning his hopes on the coming of the *Prince Rupert*. "I'm going back in her, Dave. If I can't do it one way, I will another."

"You mean you'll face the music?"

"Never—unless they catch me. Though penal servitude could be no worse than here, for the likes of me." Sam chewed his lower lip in that stubborn, nervous way he had. "As for skipping out on the company, my conscience is clear on that. I'm no slave, to be traded with never so much as 'by your leave.' I'll not give myself up. Likely some of last year's crew will still be aboard the *Prince Rupert*. If they'll let me

64

stow away to London, I'll work my passage to America somehow." Sam's face set with resolve. "That's the land for me. Wipe the slate clean and make a fresh start. And no high-and-mighty gentlemen nosing around to find out who you are and where you come from."

David nodded. "Things have turned out differently than we looked for—for both of us. But for my part, I wish you well."

Sam rubbed his hand across his scar and stared at the ground. "There's something else I have to tell you. Been meaning to for months."

David wondered what was coming.

"It's a shameful thing to say, Dave, to you who stood by me when I needed a friend the most. But after they picked me up at sea and I saw you weren't going to tell I was a runaway Gray Coat boy, I planned to use that against you. 'If ever they get me in a tight corner, he'll have to help me,' I told myself. I would hold it over you. 'It'll be bad for him if they find out who I really am, and I tell them David Thompson helped me.' " Sam hesitated. "What do you think of a fellow who'd do a trick like that?" he demanded, tortured by self-accusation and contempt.

David looked him in the eye. "But you didn't do it. I'll never believe you would, either."

"Not now, or ever. But it goes to show how one wrong move leads to another. First, I let a smuggler talk me into trying my hand at his game and then—when things look bad —I'm ready to blackmail the only real friend I've ever had to save my own skin. Like a rat, Dave, a dirty, cornered rat!" Sam spoke with loathing.

David did not know what to say. Sam McPherson had traits he would never fully understand. But it took courage to confess a thought like this. And that was all it was—a wild idea born of desperation and one that Sam would never have

65

carried out. As best he could, he told Sam how he felt.

"Well, anyway, I feel more like a man for having told you," Sam went on. "No matter what, Davvie, I'll never forget you. Who knows? Maybe I'll make my mark even yet, in America. And if I do, and the time ever comes when I can help you—"

From the headland below the fort, shouts of wild excitement startled the two. Other and nearer shouts repeated what the Indians at the headland were yelling in their native tongue and as the two boys dashed toward the gate, they saw the deputy governor bustling the native idlers out of the trade room and all but falling over himself in his haste to bolt the door.

"The *Prince Rupert!*" David told his companion. "The Indians have sighted her spars inside the river mouth. That's what they're yelling."

From buildings and wigwams people were streaming and the two young friends were sprinting for the path leading to the headland when the Governor appeared, bawling Sam's name.

"He'll want you to hoist the ensign," David said. "Too bad. See you later," he flung over his shoulder, and kept on running.

There were no routine duties at Fort Churchill that day. Governor Hearne ordered Mr. Prince to man the sloop and help tow the *Prince Rupert* to its mooring, and at a wink from Mr. Prince David jumped aboard. A mile or so downriver, the oarsmen of the sloop brought her alongside the ship. While a line was passed, David was astounded to see Geordie Charles grinning down at him over the rail. "There's six of us," Geordie sang out. "Six more Gray Coat apprentices, to help you out with your surveying. You can't be getting on with it fast enough to suit the company!"

The same old Geordie, David thought, wondering if his friend realized how ironic his joke must sound. "Did I look as green as he does, a year ago now?" he asked Mr. Prince.

"Every whit as green, with your white face and town clothes."

With her topsails bellying to the occasional puffs of wind from the open bay, the ship made excellent time up the channel, and as he bent to his oar David's excitement grew. There must be favorable news in the dispatches this year, or why these six apprentices? And if some major exploration was being planned, the past year of inactivity and bafflement might not have been wasted, after all—

And then a realization, cold as steel, clutched him. Geordie and five others from the school, every one of whom knew Sam McPherson! To what extent now, and against such odds, dare Sam rely on the disguise of his disfigurement? And if *they* recognized him, while he, who had seen Sam almost every day for the past year, had not exposed him to the Governor—

"It'll be bad for him if they find out who I really am." Sam's words, weighed now with sinister truth, returned to him in full force. His brain became a turmoil of apprehension so that this day, long and eagerly anticipated, turned to one of dread. "One wrong move leads to another," Sam had said. "But what was I to do?" David asked himself. "If the ship's master himself did not consider it his duty to turn poor Sam over to—to Execution Dock! I'd have loathed myself for the rest of my life if I'd toadied, if I'd squealed— been the one to have him swing for it."

Like the average man of his day and age, David Thompson looked on the king's imposition of prohibitive duties against trade with France as tyranny. It was this king and his minions whose domineering contempt for his subjects had cost him the American colonies. And the battle cry of no taxation without representation was echoed in England itself by an attitude of growing protest which could be measured by the great extent of the smuggling trade. Not that smugglers were heroes in most people's eyes. In their ranks were desperate men, and Sam's wrongdoing, if such it were, had been in associating himself with them. Had not Sam already paid to the full for that mistake? But argue as he would, David could see no way out of his predicament. He had been a party to Sam's concealment. That was the stern, unalterable fact, quite aside from all this justification.

Astern, David glimpsed Mr. Summers standing in the *Prince Rupert's* forepeak. If only he could have felt free to ask his advice, or Mr. Prince's, or Mr. Jefferson's. What would they have done, in his place? He did not know. He would never know. What he had done, he had done. And what he had said to poor Sam a little while ago, ahead there at the fort, about facing the music, took on a terrible significance.

As soon as the anchors were down the master was rowed ashore. There was the dispatch box, there was the Governor on the bank in all his finery, everything the same as last year —even his secret about Sam the same—

"Come aboard, Mr. Prince," Mr. Summers hailed, "and bring young Thompson with you." As the sloop came alongside, there was Jem Little, a junior officer now, directing the sailors as the sloop's lines were made fast.

The six new apprentices, Jem and Mr. Summers crowded around as David vaulted the rail. There were handshakes, much laughter and a thousand questions to be answered in one and the same breath. In the talk which followed David learned that navigation and exploration had indeed become a major concern of the company's directors. Orders were for much activity in that direction.

68

"After all this talk about mapping and so on, I wondered if I'd find you still here," Mr. Summers said. "See, here's a present for you." He handed David a very fine leather-bound notebook—tooled calfskin with brass clasps. "How will that do to keep a record of your journeys?"

David found it hard to express his thanks. Now he could put his loose day-by-day jottings into permanent form. "Though I've yet to take my first journey, sir," he admitted.

"So? Well, all that will be soon altered. Here's the way of it. It seems that Sir Hugh Dalrymple, the colonial secretary, has been comparing Captain Cook's charts of the North Pacific with what Mr. Peter Pond, a free trader out of Boston, claims to be an accurate map he has made of the Far West. Plainly there is something very amiss, for the western end of what Mr. Pond calls Athabasca Lake is shown by him to be only one hundred miles from what Cook has charted as the shore of the Pacific. Now, to get at the truth, our company is being asked—nay, commanded—to fix the true position of the west end of the Athabasca."

"That's the way of it, Dave," Jem declared. "For the proof, see all this scurrying to send out more apprentices."

Had it not been for his apprehension over Sam's secret, David could scarcely have been made happier than by such great news. He had to think, and think fast. Any moment now the new apprentices would be ordered ashore. Jem had given him a letter from his mother and, going to the bow, he leaned against the capstan and read it hurriedly.

"A weaver's life grows harder still, in England," she wrote. "For your sake and for the children's my fervent hope is that you will win advancement and soon be in a position to provide some small help for them."

His family's predicament brought a stab of self-accusation. A great project of exploration had been ordered. His chance had come at last. Had he thrown all that away, to shield a

69

friend? "Why did that sea fight have to happen when it did?" he protested fearfully. "And why did I have to be aboard this ship when Sam was rescued?" Why—why—a thousand why's—and nothing sure except that only a miracle could prevent Sam's being recognized, and his part in all that sorry business brought to the Governor's attention!

David's apprehension mounted when the time actually came for the apprentices to be transported ashore. With Mr. Prince's permission, David went with them. But during all the time they were being shown their quarters and their belongings were being carried up, Sam did not show himself. With the Governor entertaining the ship's master in his house, that was understandable. Sam would be kept busy waiting on table. When evening came and Sam had not appeared outside the Governor's house, David concluded there was no need to warn him. Either he had seen the six Gray Coats or had overheard them mentioned during the table talk. Early in the morning, before the new arrivals were up, he would contrive to meet Sam and together they might hit on some plan.

The new hands had turned in and David, who had been on late duty tallying cargo as it came ashore, was about to follow their example when a native brought word that the Governor wanted him. The summons at such a late hour filled him with fresh apprehension. A half-breed was swabbing down the kitchen, with Sam nowhere in sight. Had the dispatches revealed Sam's identity? Or Geordie or some other of the boys—had they let the cat out of the bag? David wondered as, sick at heart, he presented himself before the Governor.

"My orders are to transfer you to York Factory immediately," the Governor told him. "Two packet Indians, couriers

70

from York, will guide you. You will be in readiness to start by the morning."

That was all. Not a word about Sam, no good-bye, no explanation. But it could have been a thousand times worse. On his way back across the parade ground, he met Mr. Jefferson coming from the trade room. "Don't imagine your transfer is any of the Governor's doing," he said. "The master told me what's afoot, and the Governor doesn't like it. He wants no competitors, even young and inexperienced ones, invading his preserve. And he'll have to do some adroit explaining to make the directors believe mapping has been impossible for any of you this last year. I'd like to know what excuses he'll cook up to square himself with our gentlemen in London." Mr. Jefferson's jaw set. "And now York has orders to send out surveying parties and Samuel Hearne, the great explorer, may not be cock of the walk much longer."

Lying wide-eyed in his bunk that night, David's heart beat faster as he visualized the tremendous undertaking being launched and knew he was to have a part in it. Like every born discoverer, whether his field be the laboratory or the unmapped places of the earth, the unknown was a perpetual challenge to him. With Young Otter last winter, he had shown he had the qualifications of a hunter. But, above all else, he was a hunter of facts, of first-hand experiences. An unanswered problem in mapping or mathematics, the location of a river's source, the discovery of a lake or mountain range fascinated him as much as the hunting of rabbit, fox or partridge.

And now the greatest hunt of years was to be launched—the hunt which would fix for all time the basic point of half a continent! Had it not been for the threat of Sam being sent home in irons, this would be the happiest moment of his life. "If only I hadn't let myself get mixed up in that!"

he thought. If only— But he had, and he knew that if he had it to do again, he never could have forgiven himself had he betrayed his friend.

Suddenly he stiffened. A shape had ghosted across the oblong of moonlight in the guardhouse doorway. David slipped from his bunk and went out. It was Young Otter, who handed him a scrap of paper, then disappeared into the shadows.

"TO DAVE, READ AND DESTROY" he managed to decipher on the outside. And inside the fold: "HAVE JOINED A PARTY OF TRAPPERS RETURNING TO THE MUSKRAT COUNTRY. HOPE TO REACH AMERICA BY WAY OF THE LAKES. I WILL NEVER FORGET YOU. SAM"

CHAPTER EIGHT

A‌T THAT TIME of year the
nights were so short they were mere pauses between the
crowded days, and at two o'clock David lifted the flap of
Young Otter's wigwam and asked him to find the two Indian couriers. "I'm all packed and ready. I'll be waiting for
them here."

When his native friend had nodded and gone off in the
direction of the main encampment, David wished very much
he could have risked a good-bye to his white friends inside

the fort. But if Sam's disappearance had been discovered, it would be better for him to leave like this.

"Where was he when he gave you that paper?" he asked when Young Otter returned with the two sleepy guides.

"Two miles upriver. I was fishing. He was in a big canoe with four of the Muskrat Country people. He asked them to wait while he wrote it."

David gave Young Otter a long look. "You know?"

Young Otter nodded. "I know only he is your friend. That is enough. I am sorry for him here. He was treated worse than the packet Indians. The North West Company sends fur brigades north to the Muskrat Country. There are trails, good rivers. He will escape. Many whites go over to the North-Westers. We are not well used here. Some day I may go over to them, too." With dignity and an odd gentleness, Young Otter held out his hand. "My heart is heavy to see you go away. We have been friends."

As he gripped the outstretched hand, a tightness came to David's throat. This companionship had been one of the few bright spots in his first bitterly disappointing year. "We will stay friends," he declared simply.

"Brothers," Young Otter replied softly. "Because you never look down on us, you will always find friends among our race—friends where most whites find only enemies. The Great Spirit guards ones like you. David Thompson is good medicine for the poor Indian people. I will not forget." And withdrawing his hand with a reluctance beyond mere words, Young Otter turned and went inside the wigwam.

An hour later, the canoe which had ferried them across the river had disappeared into the early morning mists on the water and David was alone with the two packet Indians who would be his companions on the one-hundred-and-fifty mile overland journey southward. They had not been an hour on the trail before he learned how their dealings with, and dependence on, the white traders had demoralized them.

In his record of that trip across muskeg and along the swampy shoreline of the bay, he wrote in the notebook Mr. Summers had given him: "Unfortunately a gallon of very strong grog had been given to these Indians who, as usual, as soon as they landed began drinking and were soon drunk and the day lost."

Even with the best of companions, this trip down the length of the great swamp would have been a hard one. The country was so flat that, at the height of the sub-Arctic tides, the blind channels for miles inland were flooded. Muskeg and belts of black spruce, their lower branches draped with the moss known as "old man's beard," made constant detouring necessary. There were tangles of windfalls and drowned timber to fight through, and the tundra moss soaked moccasins and buckskin leggings at every step. To make his first overland journey with two drink-crazed Indians was a stiff test for the fifteen-year-old apprentice.

It was not the Indians David blamed. When sober, they were harmless, kindly fellows. He had seen the enslavement of the poor and ignorant by the grog shop owners in England, but this was worse. Young Otter had told him that, until the whites came, his race knew nothing of intoxicants. That the high and mighty gentlemen of a great company should degrade these natives for the sake of a few pennies of profit seemed to him despicable. It was an experience which strengthened the stand he took, all through his career, against his company's impoverishment and disintegration of Indians. Adding to his account of this first journey, he wrote:

"Of the native Indians along the shores of Hudson's Bay I wish to say as little as possible. The Company has the Bay in full possession and can enforce the strictest temperance of spirituous liquors, by their orders to their chief Factors. But the ships at the same time bringing out several hundred gallons of vile spirits called 'Eng. Brandy,' no such morality is thought of. No matter what service the Indian performs, or does he come to trade his Furrs, strong grog is given to him and sometimes for two or three days Men and Women are all drunk and become the most degraded of human beings."

Some years later, in David Thompson's diary this pithy entry appears:

". . . . I was obliged to take two Kegs of Alcohol by my Partners (Messrs Don^d McTavish and Joe McDonald Gart) for I had made it a law unto myself that no alcohol should pass the mountains in my company, and thus be clear of the sad sight of drunkenness and its many evils; but these gentlemen insisted upon alcohol being the most profitable article that could be taken for Indian trade. In this I knew they had miscalculated. Accordingly when we came to the defiles of the Mountains, I placed the two Kegs of Alcohol on a vicious horse; and by noon the Kegs were empty, and in pieces, the Horse rubbing his load against the Rocks to get rid of it. I wrote my partners what I had done; and that I would do the same to every Keg of Alcohol, and for the six years I had charge of the furr trade on the west side of the Mountains, no further attempt was made to introduce spirituous liquors."

On the second day after leaving Fort Churchill, the two packet Indians, though sick and wretched from their bout of drinking, said they felt well enough to go on. The three had to travel without food, for Governor Hearne had forbidden them to take any from the stores and had allowed David only one blanket for the cold, wet trip. Day after day, they splashed through the willows and drowned spruce and across the sodden tidal meadows. At nights they tried to find a hummock to camp on. However, such spots of slightly higher ground were rare and usually the trio took what rest they could on a bed of poles and brush where the moss was so flooded that a fire was impossible.

As they traveled southward, they hunted constantly for food. Ducks and geese were by no means plentiful, but David had learned well from Young Otter the secrets of stalking. His two companions, weak and listless for days after their debauch, had no heart for hunting, and it was mainly due to the white youth's persistence and skill that the party ate at all.

This was his first real testing as a hunter, and his success made him more than ever grateful to Young Otter. "An explorer must live off the country," he thought. His imagination was fired by all the talk of Athabasca exploration, and he turned the hardships of this trip into an experience which would help him during the coming weeks when, as he imagined, the factor at York would assign him to join the westward quest.

Polar bears were frequent along the boulder-strewn shoreline. On no day did they pass fewer than twelve and once David counted fifteen. But though they would often turn and face the party, only one attacked. This bear was feasting on the carcass of a stranded white whale and it charged toward them. David kept his gun at the ready as they backed away step by step. "We're hungry—but not hungry enough to want to share your rotten whale meat," he told the surly creature.

The day following this encounter the party reached the mouth of the Nelson River. The Indians had a canoe cached there and, after making the crossing, a four-mile tramp through stunted evergreens brought them to the stockade of York Factory.

When David reported to Mr. Colen, the deputy factor, the latter called to a fair-haired youth who, quill in hand, was perched on a high stool beneath the window at the far side of the room. "Jennings, this is Thompson, the new apprentice. Show him to his quarters," he instructed.

"Don't remember me, do you?" David grinned as the two crossed the yard together.

Jack Jennings took a closer look. "I do now," he said somewhat loftily, as if he were still a senior and David a mere lower school boy. "Fact is, I'd heard you were at Churchill and I wondered if you were the same snub-nosed Thompson who was always getting underfoot at school."

"Oh, come down off your high horse!" David laughed. Jennings had always been like that—a bit superior, but a decent enough sort when you broke through his reserve.

Jennings grinned back, smoothing his well-greased hair. "I see old Hearne hasn't broken *your* spirit. How are you anyway, Thompson? I'm glad to see you. Has the *Rupert* arrived? What's the news?" Jack was all interest now.

"Geordie Charles and five others have been sent out. We hadn't time for much talk. School gossip mostly. Then the Governor sent me packing."

"And with precious little on your back, at that," Jack said, glancing at David's meager load.

"It was enough, coming through those swamps. Traveling light seems to be the way they do things out here. And I suppose a fellow has to get used to native customs, if he's to get ahead."

Jennings gave him a superior smile. "You're only a year out from England. I talked like that when I was green. But if you're wise, you'll not adapt yourself any more than you must to native customs. A fellow mustn't lower his standards."

With his hopes high for the Athabasca venture, words like these from a senior apprentice were disconcerting. But then, Jennings was the sort who seldom allowed himself to be enthusiastic over anything. He couldn't really mean it, and

78

when he learned, from the dispatches the couriers had brought, of the exploration ordered by the London offices—

The two were entering the juniors' room—a surprisingly comfortable place, after the guardhouse at Churchill—and David saw a slight young man rise up from the corner bunk. "Alf, this is Thompson," Jennings explained. "I dare say you won't remember him. He's just been telling me he wants to excel in native ways." Jennings seemed to think this a very good joke indeed.

Alf Robinson nodded. "I'd drop such storybook fancies, if I were you," he advised when he had shaken hands with David. "That is, unless you want to say good-bye to even the slight comforts of life around a fort. If you want to get ahead out here, you'd better change your tune."

David sat down on his pack. His moccasins and leggings were still caked with muskeg mud, his face and hands grimy with campfire smoke and dotted with mosquito bites. "I don't understand—"

"If Factor Marten thought you could look after yourself in the woods, you'd be done for properly," Alf warned him. "Whatever you do, Thompson, don't let him hear you talk like that." He lowered his voice. "Jack and I are apprentices, like yourself. We're not permitted to know much of company plans. But we do happen to know that the governors in London have been getting after old Marten to set up posts in the Far West before those confounded Nor'westers cut off our trade completely. Something will have to be done. But who, in his right senses, would learn enough of Indian ways to have himself banished to that wilderness?"

CHAPTER NINE

D AVID HAD BEEN hearing of this rival company increasingly during the past year. "Wolves of the North" some called them. The fall of Quebec to General Wolfe in 1759 had destroyed the French trade in furs, and for a time the Hudson's Bay Company had enjoyed its old-time monopoly. But then, in 1784, the very year of young Thompson's arrival, a group of adventurers, calling themselves the North West Company, had been formed and had set up headquarters in Montreal. From that highly strategic point, these independent traders had launched a vigorous conquest of the West and North.

Instead of waiting for the Indians to come hundreds of miles down the rivers with their furs, which was what the staid and unprogressive governors of David's company had been doing, these Nor'westers had been, of late, thrusting ever deeper into the rich fur country in a cunningly planned outflanking move. They were a vigorous, daring lot, and this last season had managed to skim the cream of the Hudson's Bay Company's trade.

Then, too, there was an additional fact which the governors in London found particularly annoying. Many of the Nor'westers, Scots for the most part, had been former employees of the Hudson's Bay Company and had learned the fur trade while in their service. For one reason or another, they had quit the company's ranks and had struck out for themselves. The inside knowledge which they had previously gained had been put to such good use in planning their future campaign that they had become a thorn in the flesh of the comfortable gentlemen in London who were directing the destinies of the long-established company. So much so that, if Alf were to be believed, they were now insisting that Factor Marten launch some counter-move.

"You speak of banishment," David commented. "You've seen the country yonder to the west?"

"Not I," Robinson assured him. "Nor do I want to, for from all I've heard, life there is primitive beyond description."

"If you ask me, what these Nor'westers are doing is hardly cricket," Jennings commented. "Why, until they took the bit between their teeth like this, we could stay safely inside our forts and make the Indians come to us. But now, the way matters are going—"

An angry bellowing from the yard interrupted him. "What on earth?" David asked. "Do you keep cattle here?"

"Cattle?" Jack Jennings grinned. "I say! You *are* green."

81

"Well," David explained, "it sounds to me like an enraged bull."

The two senior apprentices burst out laughing. "It is," Jack told him, "though not of the sort you think. No need to be alarmed. You'll soon grow used to his bellowings—and worse."

"It's Factor Marten," Alf said. "Here, take a look." He crossed the room and, opening the door a few inches, beckoned to David. "Another poor devil is feeling the weight of the old tyrant's fists."

David peered out in time to see one of the packet Indians who had come with him from Churchill reel backwards, blood streaming from his mouth and nose from the blow the burly Marten had just dealt him. Then, as he crumpled to the packed earth of the yard, the factor's heavy boot took him in the ribs with sickening impact.

"I'll teach you—you mangy pup!" The factor's face was bloated with rage. "Talk back to me, will you? Take this." And as the Indian swayed to his feet, Marten's fist struck him down again. This time he lay quiet. Marten stood, his short legs spread, sucking a skinned knuckle and glaring down at the prostrate form. Then he spat contemptuously and walked away.

"Best close the door," Jennings whispered urgently. "He's not above taking it out on us."

The thoughtful Robinson bit his thin lips. "Vindictive and oppressive to the last degree," he muttered. His voice was trembling. "After all his twenty-four years in the country, he has not a single friend, neither white nor Indian."

"Nor wants one," Jack added. "Oh, well, what can't be cured must be endured." His tone hinted that David would be wise to forget the incident.

But the Welsh boy could not forget. Governor Hearne, with all his faults, was preferable to this. He was more than

82

ever glad that, following all this talk of an expedition westward, he would soon be free of such a tyrant.

However, as the days became weeks and he saw no move to outfit such a party, David had to face the fact that he must endure a winter at York Factory. As the fall advanced, he had additional reason to be thankful to Young Otter for the wood lore he had taught him, because when the fall goose hunt began, young Thompson's marksmanship and stalking skill soon caused Mr. Colen to assign him to a place among the regular hunters.

The nights had become sharp and frosty, the mosquito season was over and though on bright days the black flies proved bothersome, it was exhilarating to be out ranging the ponds and sloughs from dawn until dark. The geese were in prime condition after a summer of rich feeding on the northern tundras. David had the hearty appetite of every growing boy, and the game he and the others brought in provided a delightful change in the fare of the junior mess.

"It's the fortunate family in England that can afford even a goose on Christmas day," he said with a grin one evening as he munched away on a fat and juicy drumstick. "Yet here we dine like lords."

"I wish the boys back at the school could see us now," Jack agreed. "They needn't feel sorry for me. In some ways the fur trader's life is not so bad. It would have been salt horse and ship's bread without end had they sent us to sea instead of to the Hudson's Bay."

Even the studious Alf was fond of the sport. The surplus of their daily bags was hung in the storehouse for winter use and for a fortnight the three Gray Coat boys had good times together.

Winter closed in early that year, and when the ponds were locked in ice and the last of the geese had gone, Mr. Colen detailed Jack and David to take an Indian and his wife and

set out on a more ambitious hunt. They were given a wigwam, fowling pieces, fish hooks and lines, traps, snares, blankets and three weeks' salt provisions. And as David helped
carry the outfit from the storeroom and load it on the hand
sleds, he told himself that at last this expedition looked like
"the real thing."

"You will proceed up river to the large stream we call
French Creek," the deputy, Mr. Colen, instructed. Then
added with a friendly smile, "I think you'll enjoy this, young
Thompson."

"I'm sure I shall, sir," David answered. The way he had
acquitted himself on the fall goose hunt had more than once
won him Mr. Colen's commendation. David had at first been
puzzled by the deputy's somewhat bewildering changes in
manner. With the juniors, in the privacy of their quarters,
he seemed free-and-easy; yet when Factor Marten was about
he might storm and dominate those under him. Latterly, however, David had concluded Mr. Colen knew what he was
doing. Any sign of softness on his part certainly would not
have been tolerated by the bull-necked tyrant who had them
all in his power. No doubt Mr. Colen's pleasant ways when in
private were meant to make up for the brusqueness he felt
he must display in front of their superior.

When they had loaded the second sled, the Indian ran outside the palisade and brought in a fine Newfoundland dog
that David had never seen before.

"Wherever did you get that splendid fellow?" Mr. Colen
asked.

"I trade him, with our people yonder," the Indian explained, pointing eastward across the bay.

"The natives have a few dogs like that on the Labrador,"
Mr. Colen told the boys. "And how fine they are compared to
the wolf dogs so common here! Useful, too," he added, as the
Indian harnessed the great animal to one of the sleds. "With

84

his help, you should reach your hunting grounds tonight."

Black Boy, the Newfoundland, proved a real help that day. He was a strong and willing worker, in harness or out of it, and by the time that French Creek was reached, late in the day, both the apprentices were keen about him.

"I don't see why Alf prefers fort life to a trip like this," David said as the two brought their axes from the sled and began helping the Indians make camp. The site chosen was in a snug clump of jackpines on the west side of the creek mouth. And in the stillness, as their axe blows began ringing out and the tree shadows lay long across the snow, the factor's tyranny and the restrictions of fort life were forgotten. Here, in company with his Indian friends, David Thompson was sharing a way of life which had prevailed throughout the Northland for centuries before the white man came. Here your survival did not depend on anyone expect yourself; here skill and patience and endurance were what counted most. Those who could learn what the wilderness had to teach need have no fear; those who could not or would not learn must either endure misery and hardship or else retreat to the safety and deadening monotony of fort life.

Jack rested on his axe. "Oh, a few weeks of hunting and fishing is well enough—makes one feel quite the English gentleman with our two natives to do the fetching and carrying."

David kept on trimming tepee poles. "Why fool ourselves? The Indian and his wife are the real masters here. Babes in the wood—that's all we are until we, too, master forest ways."

Jennings shrugged. "The more you do, the more they'll let you do."

David did not argue with him. But he thought that the more they would teach him, the better he would like it.

"You don't agree with me, I see," Jennings said.

David sunk his axe into a jackpine stump and straightened his back. "I'll not be content until I'm as good or better at this kind of thing than the Indians themselves. I want to be my own master. That's what I could never be in England. And no man's free who must ride on another's back."

"Everyone to his own notions," Jack commented airily, and began to whistle.

Next morning, after the wigwam had been made comfortable and a supply of dry wood cut, the Indian asked David to help him build the "hoard." This was a pyramid-like structure of heavy logs, six feet square at the base and narrowing to a two-foot opening five feet above the ground, where a lid of stout timber was secured.

"S'pose bear come—we fool him." The Indian grinned. He gave David to understand that inside this cache the frozen trout, hare and ptarmigan would be stored until the first sled load was ready to be hauled to the food depot at the fort.

As the work progressed, David learned how to notch and saddle the ends of the logs so that no marauder could tear them apart. For months now his axemanship had been improving. Frozen wood does not lend itself to accurate hewing, but nevertheless most of his corners passed inspection, and the Indian soon saw that here was one apprentice who did not shirk the heavy work. For though no equal to the man in strength, David put his back into the chore and did his share of the heaving and carrying.

Once the hoard was finished, the hunting party set its snares along the runways of the "snowshoe rabbits" and while Jack and the Indian woman tended the set lines on the ice above the fishing pools, the man took David across the willow flat to locate a good place to set their bird net.

This, as David soon saw, was an undertaking for an expert. Ptarmigan tracks were everywhere among the willow clumps, yet his guide and teacher scouted the heavier meadows and smaller openings for a mile before choosing a spot on which to set the net. David had never taken part in a bird drive, but to hear Jack and Alf talk about one in their quarters of an evening, it sounded simple enough. Now, however, he realized how many factors must be taken into account. The quantity and freshness of the bird tracks, the feeding grounds in the immediate area, wind direction, time and duration of winter sunlight, all these had to be considered.

By the white man's standards, this Indian was ignorant, yet the observant young apprentice realized there was no officer in the fort who could do what the man was doing now. Even the factor, with his bullying and floggings, was utterly dependent on these people for the food he ate, the furs which clothed him, the fuel which kept him warm.

Dusk was falling as they snowshoed back to camp. An arctic owl ghosted over the dark spires of the jackpines and from across the river came the long-drawn-out hunting call of wolves. Then from the woods ahead there came the welcome scent of campfire smoke and with a friendly bark, Black Boy came bounding through the snow to meet them.

As David lifted the wigwam flap, saw the grouse breasts grilling over the fire, and felt the welcome warmth, a deep, sure sense of content came over him.

"This is home," he said to the Indian woman, in her own language.

Her brown, flat face broke into a smile. This young white man was not like the others. He was always ready to find out how the Indians did things and did not consider himself above learning their language. Out in the woods like this, a friendliness and a feeling of confidence seemed to pass between the Indians and him. How much better life would be for her people, if all whites were as this one was! But she only said, "You have done well today."

Warming his shins beside the fire, David looked across and returned her smile. In all his months in this wild land he had never felt so secure, so sure of himself.

87

CHAPTER TEN

Though David Thompson was
too young to realize it, this feeling of security was prompted
by something far more than the primitive comforts of a hunting camp. Firelight, warmth and food after a day's work in
the wintry woods are always reassuring. But this went deeper.
It came, in fact, from his sense of harmony with his surroundings. And this, in turn, was the result of early teaching, whole-
heartedly accepted. Thanks to his mother's religious training, he never doubted but that the world was the work of an
all-wise Creator. And through mathematics he had come to
see that all things in it obeyed a natural law.

To trust and act upon such beliefs in a society just beginning to emerge from a long era of superstition made for humbleness, and at the same time gave one a strange audacity. In an era when a lingering belief in witchcraft and black magic held many minds in bondage, to rule one's life as if the universe were governed, not by whim and supernatural malice, but by the law of cause and effect, took courage and a faith which to many seemed little short of simple-mindedness and childish naïveté. The white men inside the forts spoke and acted as if the wilderness were sinister and hostile—an ever-lurking enemy to pit oneself against, never something that could be understood and co-operated with. For months the influence of such behavior on the part of his superiors had been strong upon David. But now, in the hunting camp, these hampering doubts were swept away. A sincere trust in God and the exercise of his own intelligence had freed him. And from that winter on, no matter in what wild, untraveled parts of the North he found himself, David Thompson could be fortified by the assurance that he was not forgotten or the pawn of blind chance. He had entered into the birthright of every true explorer.

A week later when, by means of snares, their ptarmigan drives and daily fishing through the ice, the hoard was filled, the Indian harnessed his Newfoundland and set off with the load, nearly a day's travel down the river ice.

It was the next evening, while awaiting his return, that the raider came. Jack and David were inside the wigwam while the woman cooked their supper of grouse and salt pork. Suddenly, in the firelight, the boys saw her crouch. She gave a warning hiss and pointed to the open door flap.

David moved on hands and knees across the pine branches with which the ledge was floored. As he neared the opening, he heard a scuffling in the snow.

"Sounds like something big," Jennings, close behind him, whispered. "Careful now. Can you see?"

After the firelight, it was difficult to make out who or what their visitor was. Certainly they had not heard a sled approaching, but until his eyes became accustomed to the dusk, David fancied it must be Black Boy. Perhaps he had slipped his collar and romped home ahead of his master. Then his throat went tight as he made out the gigantic white figure swaying within a few feet of the door, vaguely outlined against the whiter snow.

"A polar bear! He smells the cooking," he gasped. "Quick, Jack—the musket!"

David thrust out his hand behind him and kept feeling for the weapon, for by now the raider's head and hulking shoulders were blocking the doorway.

It was the Indian woman who slid the musket within David's grasp. The bear's eyes were on him as, inch by inch, he dragged the long barrel forward, aimed and squeezed the trigger. All that happened was a sickening click, for the priming had become too wet to fire.

The Indian woman crouched, her eyes bright as those of a trapped creature—but a creature who would fight. From the corner of one eye, David saw her fingers close around the axe handle.

By now the wigwam was shuddering as the bear tried to squeeze between the two poles of the doorway. "Now!" the Indian woman screamed. As she raised the axe, David whirled the musket end for end and together they clubbed the outstretched muzzle with all their might.

After his first swing, David realized he had broken the musket off at the stock. Now it was a fight for life. Though the poles still held, the bared fangs and savage eyes warned what would happen if the bear closed with them. The woman's axe struck again and again, so savagely it left David little room

90

to swing. Then, in one wild lunge, he drove the musket barrel into the gaping mouth. The bear's teeth closed on it and it was wrenched from David's grasp.

However, the thrust had its effect, for the bear backed away a pace or two, coughing. The woman gave David the axe and he ducked through the doorway and fetched the great creature a stunning blow between the eyes. The animal shook its head and seemed about to charge when the woman shoved a fowling piece within David's reach. Not until he fired did he realize that she had withdrawn the bird shot and loaded it with two balls. The bear stumbled, wheeled crazily and sprawled on the trampled snow.

As he stood watching the dying animal, David heard a yell, half-rage, half-derision, from inside the wigwam, and when he looked in he saw the Indian woman leap and clutch some dangling object in the shadows of the roof. It was one of Jack Jennings' legs and as she rained abuse upon him she dragged the senior apprentice from the smokehole. Down Jack came and she would have set upon him had not David come to his rescue.

"Paugh!" the woman sneered. "You—you call yourself a man?"

It was to Jack Jennings' credit that he did not try to explain away his panic. He must have known how scathing was the contempt of these native women for cowardice in a man. Some apprentices, accustomed to browbeating Indians from across the counter, might have ordered her to hold her tongue. But the easygoing, comfort-loving Jack at least had the courage to make no weak excuses for himself.

"There, now," Jack protested with a sheepish grin. "No need to rub it in. I've never claimed to be a hunter." He turned to David. "Every Indian for miles will know about this before the week is out. But what I'm concerned with mainly is that it does not reach the factor's ears. Do you think that beads or some present or other might induce her not to tell?"

"Why not talk it over with Alf?" David suggested. "He'd know. Though I very much doubt if any of the Indians will ever tell the factor. They're too afraid of him for that."

Later, when the hunt was over and the two apprentices were back on duty in the fort, it was plain enough that David had guessed correctly. However, the report of the incident which had spread among the Indians was quite another matter. News travels far and swiftly among native peoples, and David was not long in concluding that his part, at least, was known to many. As the weeks passed, it was surprising how frequently the old men and the best hunters went out of their way to teach him some further piece of native skill, so that by the time spring arrived he had been initiated into many a forest secret and had mastered skills which many a veteran trader had not the patience to acquire. Tracking, the proper way to weave babiche and main filling into a snowshoe frame, the lore of winter fishing, and how to tell the weather in advance—these and other things his native friends taught him so thoroughly that Alf Robinson cautioned him about it.

"Don't be so enthusiastic. Better watch yourself or you'll go completely native, Dave. Every so often some poor devil of a white who's gone over to the Indians shows up at the fort. He's forgotten how to be a white man, and he can't turn completely Indian. Fact is, he's made himself an outcast. Why, only last week, when you were out hunting, one like that showed up with a party from the Muskrat Country."

David felt his nerves go taut. "You saw him? Talked to him?" He was sitting cross-legged on a bearskin before the guardroom fire. He did not dare look up. Sam, with his aversion for wilderness life, unable to find his way south to the lake region, an exile in the Muskrat Country!

"An old fellow, bearded like Noah. He's been here before."

David's tenseness ebbed from him. But it *could* have been Sam McPherson. The Muskrat Country was not so far from here.

"Another thing," Alf went on. "No officer of the company, even a junior one, should bring himself down to the level of these people. No white can do these primitive, menial things as well as they can. And when he fumbles, he's bound to lose their respect."

David made no answer. But he did not agree. The respect Alf meant was based on fear, and he wanted none of that. There was, however, another kind of respect born of comradeship and a conviction that, beneath their skins, men everywhere had much in common. When you took men as you found them, harboring no prejudices, they very often took you in the same way. They judged you for what you were, and not by your position or the color of your skin.

With Alf it was different. Alf aspired to be what was called a "gentleman." But David Thompson knew he himself lacked those social graces which often make promotion easier to win. During this last year he had grown a good two inches and his short, rather bony figure had filled out, thanks to his outdoor life and a diet which was more suited to the needs of a growing youth than that supplied in charity schools. Even so, with his angular shoulders, his square face with its high cheekbones and his unruly, oddly-cut hair, there was an awkwardness to his appearance which would always make him seem out of place in drawing rooms and sumptuously furnished offices.

"I'm not 'going native,' as you call it," David answered. "But when the ice goes, surely this year Factor Marten will send that expedition westward. And my chances of being chosen for it should certainly be better if I know some Indian ways instead of still being a green apprentice."

93

"For my part, I doubt if the factor will ever send such an expedition," Alf said forthrightly.

"But you yourself told me the governors in London were expecting him to do so," David protested.

Alf favored him with a knowing wink. "Our company is interested solely in trade. All this talk of mapping, of exploration! In my opinion it doesn't suit the company's designs at all."

"It's the Colonial Office in London does the urging," Alf insisted. "All our company is doing is making a show of bending to their demands." The look he gave David had something of impatience in it. "There are times, my boy, when you are too literal-minded, too simple for your own good. Why should the company want the country westward opened up? Furs, barter, oh, yes! But making maps for your rivals to travel by—that's like handing over the keys of one's own treasure house. And our London gentlemen are no fools."

David stared. Perhaps, as Alf had just remarked, he was too direct-minded and simple for his own good. Such intrigue and double-dealing left him all at sea.

"Don't you ever fool yourself," Alf was saying, "it's a deep game our governors are playing. And if you doubt it, just you think back to what that classmate of yours, Geordie Charles, told you when he landed at Churchill last autumn."

"What's this? What's this?" Jack Jennings called out from the far corner of the room where he had been dozing on one of the bunks. "I didn't hear—"

"Then I'll enlighten you," Alf broke in. "Here's the story, just as Davvie gave it me. Dave here is so gullible he didn't understand, though I confess that, even at that time, it all made sense to me." Then Alf explained how, though Geordie Charles had no bent for mathematics, he had been sent out by the company as a trained navigator. "The joke being, of course," Alf ended, "that with scores of naval officers on half-

94

pay cooling their heels in England—any one of whom would have jumped at the chance to do such work—the company chooses a dullard from the Gray Coat school."

"How much training did Geordie really have, I wonder?" Jack asked.

"Well," David admitted, "it couldn't have been much. From what he told me, they crammed him with a smattering of algebra, gave him three short lessons with a quadrant, declared him fully competent and shipped him out."

The two youths grinned knowingly. "And still you don't see why the company adopted such a ruse?"

David pushed his square cut hair back off his forehead. "Not unless—"

Triumphantly Alf finished the sentence for him. ". . . unless our company intends to keep the geography of this land a deep, dark secret. And that, my simple-minded Davvie, is precisely what they intend to do."

As soon as the spring breakup was over, Indians from the interior began coming down-river to trade their winter's furs. Jack and Alf and David were kept busy behind the counter, for hardly a day passed without a fresh brigade of canoes arriving. Out of the vast country to the west and north they came, their birchbarks gunwale deep, women, girls and all but the smallest children helping with the paddling. Early and late they thronged the trade room, their mild, observant eyes bright with wonder. From what far places had they come? the young apprentice wondered. Down what unmapped waterways had their canoes threaded their way? What was the country like back there? And would his own eyes ever see it?

In early summer others besides the dusky dwellers of that land came to York Factory from the West. There was Wil-

95

liam Tomison, the rugged Scot who for years had been chief inland for the company in the Saskatchewan country. With him was Robert Longmore, a reserved, purposeful officer, and the chief inland's second-in-command. Mitchell Oman, a bearded and experienced trader, arrived with them. Soon the rumor spread that big events were in the making.

Until daylight on the night of their arrival, the lights burned in the quarters of Factor Marten. It was a close and starless night, with a humidity and stillness about it which magnified sound. David, who had dropped off to sleep promptly, was roused several hours later by someone shaking him by the shoulder.

"Pull on your breeches and step outside with Alf and me," Jack urged. In the darkness his voice was edged with anxiety. "By the sound of things, there's trouble brewing in the factor's quarters."

David rubbed his eyes and sat up.

"The gentlemen from inland are out for blood tonight, it seems like," Jack said. "Mr. Colen's with them, and old Marten is blasting them fit to raise the roof."

David, barefooted, followed Jack outside. For a moment or two, there was only an indistinct, angry rumble of voices.

"What has all this to do with us?" David asked sleepily. The gathering had all the signs of a carouse.

"It's our duty to stand by," Alf insisted. "Even before he went across to join the others, Mr. Colen was plainly worried. You know how readily old Marten can whip himself into a towering rage. And the gentlemen from inland are not the sort to knuckle under. Mitchell Oman's as wild and untamed as the territory he roams. So mark my words, Mr. Colen may need reinforcements if he tries to make peace between the likes of them. Neither side will yield an inch."

David stood with the two senior apprentices in the shadows, listening to the angry voices. For several days, Factor Marten

96

had scarcely shown himself out-of-doors. And when he had, his bloodshot eyes and sodden appearance betrayed the fact that he was fighting a losing bout with his old enemy, grog.

Suddenly the factor's outraged bellowing drowned the other angry voices. He swore a fearful oath and accused someone of "mutiny." There was the stamping of feet and the crash of benches and tables being knocked over.

The three apprentices ran to the window and in the light of the candles from within David saw Alf's chin tremble. "There's nothing—we—"

"Mr. Longmore, watch out!" Jack yelled. "Quick—behind you! He's got a knife!" He charged for the door. David was about to follow him. He saw the glint of the factor's dirk, saw Mr. Colen try to seize the upraised arm, heard Jack shout that the door was bolted.

"This way!" David shouted. His bare feet found footing in the chinks of the log wall and he half-jumped, half-fell, over the sill and into the melee of pounding feet and struggling bodies.

Oman, staggering to his feet, with blood seeping into his wild beard from a gash in his forehead, snatched up a three-legged stool and hurled it. It missed Marten's head by inches. Mr. Colen, still gripping Marten's wrist, was being carried off his feet and in danger of having the dirk buried in his own throat. David vaulted the overturned table, threw himself like a terrier at Marten's spread legs, and with a quick twist of arms and shoulders toppled him to the floor. Whereupon Mr. Tomison, who had been trying to hold off the enraged Oman, brought his foot down on Marten's wrist and pinned it to the floor.

"If it's fight you want, you can have your fill of it from me," he roared. "But in daylight, when you're sober."

The factor's breath came in stricken gasps. His habitual drinking made him incapable of sustained exertion, but there

97

was hate in the small, red eyes glaring up from his bloated face.

"Let him up," Oman demanded. "We'll finish this here and now. An' if it's knife play he wants—" His hand reached for his own dirk, the handle of which showed in his legging, Highland fashion.

But by now the chief inland had command of the situation. "Mr. Longmore, see Mitchell to his quarters," he ordered. Then in a quieter voice: "Thank you, Mr. Colen. Only for you this sot of a factor might have committed murder."

Mr. Tomison regarded David sternly. "This is no place for apprentices, Thompson. Off with you." Then as the youth hitched his breeches higher about his lean, brown-skinned waist and was unbarring the door, Mr. Tomison's eyes met those of Mr. Longmore. There was questioning in the glance and Mr. Longmore's slight nod answered it.

"He'll do," the chief inland agreed quietly.

CHAPTER ELEVEN

Aᴌᴛʜᴏᴜɢʜ ᴛʜᴇ ᴀᴘᴘʀᴇɴᴛɪᴄᴇs were not told the rights and wrongs of the quarrel, there was no doubt as to which side they favored. Like every bully, Marten was a coward at heart, and in his three officers from the West he had men of a different stamp from the clerks and native retainers he had become accustomed to rule so autocratically. Longmore, Tomison and Oman were, first and foremost, men of action. Their years of service in the wild Saskatchewan country had taught them to live dangerously and it was plain to the three boys that they were not the sort to indulge in the petty jealousies of fort life.

"You mark my words," Alf declared at dawn that morning when they watched the three Westerners stride from the factor's quarters, "there's more behind all this than company politics."

"I think so, too," Jack agreed. "Old Tomison had blood in his eye from the moment he stepped ashore from the brigade canoe. Y'see, David, the chief inland is supposed to take his orders from the factor here. Seems like now he's refused to do so. Or why else Marten's charge of mutiny?"

This assumption struck David as a reasonable one. And all the more so when, from the shadow of the guardhouse wall, the three saw Mr. Colen come from the factor's house and walk quickly to overtake the three visiting officers.

"I'd not want to be in the deputy's shoes," Jack remarked. "It's all very well to act the peace maker, but in this case the lot of a go-between is more than ever a thankless one."

"True enough," Alf admitted, "but Mr. Colen will smooth this over, if anyone can. He has a way with him."

This David could readily believe. It was inevitable that under a factor like Marten there must be friction, but in his own observations of the deputy, David had found him soft-spoken, even to the point of deference. And yet, without forcing the issue, he seemed usually to win out. Even in such rough surroundings, his manner was more of the courtier than the adventurer. Pleasant, tactful, he nevertheless contrived to have his own way in matters he considered important, while appearing to bow to the will of others in secondary things. Serving under such a factor, he had to be adept at playing a lone hand.

But it was not until some time later that the boys were able to discover on which side Mr. Colen stood in the present dispute. As the days passed, the rumor grew that the veteran Tomison, goaded beyond endurance by the factor's mismanagement of affairs in the Saskatchewan, had, that wild night, demanded a settling of accounts. When Marten, beside himself after his lengthy bout of solitary drinking, had called such plain talk mutiny, Tomison had, so the story went, gone him one better and resigned as chief inland.

The climax of this clash of personalities came with the arrival of the two packet Indians from Churchill. The *Prince Rupert,* helped by favorable winds, was the first company ship to reach the bay that year and Governor Hearne, always prompt in such matters, had sent the mail pouches overland.

Mail was the big event of the year, and this time the apprentices, though merely pawns in the far-flung game their superiors were playing, knew that orders of unusual importance had come.

Mrs. Thompson wrote that conditions were slightly better at home. There were more and more power looms coming into the north of England, but their output, though cheaper, was unable to compete, in fashionable London, with that of skilled hand-weavers. The Guild, she said, had given her several good orders, and she had prospects of others. Last winter had not been so cold and "the savings I have made on coals had allowed me to feed the children better. I am not letting them forget their brother in the New World. You are often in our thoughts and prayers," his mother ended.

David had his annual letter mostly written and at odd times during the next days answered his mother's questions. "There is some big undertaking afoot," he told her, "though how far it will affect me, I have yet to learn."

If only the factor would show himself! From the trade-room door, the apprentices often saw Mr. Tomison and Mr. Colen deep in talk in the shade of the senior staff quarters across the yard. Then one afternoon, Mr. Longmore and old Oman were sent for and the three Westerners went inside. A few minutes later, when David had returned to checking the accounts, a half-breed servant came with orders from Mr.

Colen for him to present himself at the staff quarters immediately.

David hurried across and entered the hewn log room. By this time the deputy had joined Tomison, Longmore and Oman. The four sat around the table and it was plain that big events were in the making.

"Sit yonder, on the bench there, Thompson," Mr. Colen said. Then, rising slowly, he spread a paper bearing the London seal on the table and cleared his throat.

"Gentlemen, Mr. Tomison already knows the contents of this document," the deputy began. "And because of it he has decided to continue his splendid service to the company." He leaned forward, his knuckles on the table, his rather high-pitched voice vibrant with controlled excitement. "I am now in a position to disclose that when the ship left last season, I felt it my bounden duty to take upon myself a full report of the state of affairs here." Mr. Colen permitted himself a slight smile. "I need not go into details, but the outcome has been that, from this day, I am factor here at York. Humphrey Marten has been recalled to England!"

Mitchell Oman, tugging at his great beard, smote the table so hard that the ink horn jumped. "Yon's the best news I've heard in many a moon, sir!" he declared.

Mr. Colen bowed deprecatingly. "Thank you. As a result, our trusted Tomison—under me—has been given increased powers as chief inland. You, Mr. Longmore, I am pleased to reveal, are hereby appointed his lieutenant. You, Mitchell Oman, will serve under Mr. Longmore and, in your turn, will have this likely lad, Thompson, as your clerk."

David could feel the blood pounding in his ears. But there was even more exciting news. "Gentlemen, being from the West, none know better than you the inroads which the Nor'westers have been making into our trade. 'Outflanking us' is the term Mr. Tomison used, both to the late factor and to me. Now, with Marten gone, you are to have your wish. You will be immediately outfitted with a large party and will leave to establish a post on the plains. In other words, in this matter of furs, the war is on."

Mr. Longmore spoke. He was a lean, slightly-built man compared with the two thickset Scots, slow-spoken but giving one a feeling of confidence by all he said and did. "Marten's pigheadedness and dallying have cost us months of precious time. But with your full support, Factor Colen, that is a handicap which may be overcome. Yonder there is an area big as a continent, waiting to be taken. I feel certain that the governors in London will have no cause to regret this step."

The black-haired, black-eyed Tomison nodded. "You've backed us, Colen, and we'll back you. But, mark my words, it won't be easy. Those wolves of the North are a wily lot."

As he sat on the bench and listened to the conversation of these veterans, David came to realize more fully that his company was pitted against an alert and daring foe. Mr. Longmore and the chief inland proved shrewd guessers of the Nor'westers' plans, and it seemed certain that if these were not foiled within the next few seasons, the flow of trade to Hudson's Bay would become a trickle and the posts there faced with ruin.

Toward the conclusion of the talk, the chief inland turned slowly in his chair and scrutinized the waiting boy. "A bit undersized, I'd say," he commented to the new factor. "But you tell me he already has a smattering of navigation?"

"So the records show. Though under Marten, and Hearne, too, with his aversion to exploring by others, he has had no chance either to improve his knowledge or to display however much of it he has."

"We'll soon change that," Tomison assured him. "I'm not questioning your choice, y'understand, but I hope you're not sending us out with a completely green apprentice. Oman and I are not the men we once were on the trail. And Long-more here is no longer a stripling—much as he would like to think so." The chief inland said this last with a wry smile. "What say to letting us add one of your senior apprentices to our party? Not that we can't use young Thompson. But a junior with more experience of the country and of native ways would not come amiss, you'll grant."

Old Oman, leaning back with his arms folded across his massive chest, tilted his Glengarry bonnet at an even more rakish angle, caught David's eye and greeted him with a ponderous wink. "Leave the lad be, sir," he said. "I've heard a tale or two in my travels. They tell me he has quite a way wi' bears. Aye—quite a way. I'm satisfied to have him as my clerk. For where we're going, we'll be needin' one who can handle weapons, no just a pen."

Mr. Colen rapped the table with finality. "You may leave us now, Thompson," he said over his shoulder, and with the air of one who has matters more weighty than the fate of a mere apprentice to discuss. When David Thompson withdrew and sprinted across the yard, he was overtaken with an all but overwhelming desire to turn a cartwheel. His snub-nosed face was shining and his feet seemed hardly to touch the ground as he sped to the guardhouse to tell Jack and Alf of his unbelievable good fortune.

Bright and early the next morning the work of outfitting the party began. All told, counting *voyageurs* and native packers and canoemen, no less than forty-six persons were detailed to make up the expedition. Fresh stores were broached, new birchbark freight canoes made ready, and supplies for a whole year parceled into packs which would stow most advantageously in the canoes and handle easiest on the hundreds of portages which lay before the party.

From dawn until dark, through most of July, David was

104

kept busy, under Mitchell Oman's immediate direction, checking the lists of trade goods, blankets, axes, weapons, kegs of powder and canvas bags of shot of varied kinds. Even when the annual ship came upriver and the work of loading and unloading taxed the staff to the utmost, Mr. Colen turned a deaf ear to the ship captain's urging that members of the expedition be detailed to help. The chief inland and all his party were greatly encouraged to see how in this, as in other ways, the new factor refused to allow anything to delay the time of departure. After years of dallying, the company was on the offensive. And at York, from factor to apprentices, it was determined to remain so.

At last, one morning in late July, the hour of embarkation came. David had shaken hands with Alf and Jack and, shouldering his personal belongings, was making his way through the crowd to the landing stage, when the Indian who had hunted with him early the previous winter touched his arm. As he turned, the Indian slipped a thong into his hand. David looked down to find Black Boy at the other end of the strap, grinning up at him with lolling tongue.

"What's this?" David asked, a bit uncertainly. "A present?"

The Indian nodded.

David stroked the Newfoundland's sleek head. "He'd be a fine companion, that I know. But with the loaded canoes, and weeks of travel against the current—"

"Take him, lad, by all means," the chief inland, who was standing near, broke in. "We need good work dogs where we're going. Newfoundlands are hard to come by yonder, and he looks the sort who'll sire us something better than the narrow-chested mongrels we've been using."

From the beach below, Mitchell Oman, who was dispatching the flotilla of canoes, shouted that David's turn had come. He gripped the hand of his Indian friend. "I'll not forget you, nor all you've taught me," he promised hastily. "I'll do my best for Black Boy."

The Indian permitted himself a slow, understanding smile. "You're a good man. Good man needs a good dog," he said in the native tongue as David moved away.

The heavier-loaded freight canoes had been dispatched first. Now there was a burst of cheering from the bank, the cannon of the fort fired a parting salute and when David, already under way, looked back, he saw the three leaders step into the last canoe. The weathered logs of the palisade and buildings glistened silver gray in the morning sunlight, the shawls and gaudy calico of the Indian women in the background lent a touch of color to the scene. He saw Factor Colen doff his plumed hat and wave a parting salute. Jack and Alf, on a pile of wood beneath the wall, were waving, shouting to him. David twirled his dripping paddle over his head in the *voyageur* gesture of farewell. Then, bracing his knees and settling himself against the thwart, he swung into the stroke of his companions. His paddle bit the water, his shoulders swung and rolled in unison with the others. Now the wooded point hid them from York Factory and the London charity boy's first great journey inland had begun.

Week after week they paddled, portaged, lined their craft up lesser rapids, camped at dusk and were on their way by dawn. Through the hunting grounds of the Bay Indians, along the Hayes River, into boisterous Lake Winnipeg and westward up the silt-laden, swirling Saskatchewan, they made their way.

Often during the brief noonday *regailes,* David would hear stories from the *voyageurs* of the old days on the plains. And around the campfire he heard from Mitchell Oman of the ghastly smallpox epidemic of 1781, in which half the Indians of that vast country had perished; of how Oman and his partners had found villages of a hundred lodges left without one living soul, and of the mongrel, half-wild dogs who feasted on the emaciated bodies; stories of great buffalo hunts and of the feuds and jealousies between the tribes with which Dave must soon learn to deal.

"Ye're lucky to be serving under Mr. Longmore," Oman confided to him one evening. The others were making camp along the bunch willow below a massive cutbank and David had gone with his immediate superior to set the net which should secure them fish after darkness fell. "None understands the Indians better. Why, man alive, he can even think in their language. He knows their weaknesses and loyalties like none other. And by his fair dealing, he has many o' them for friends. Learn from him, laddie. For, mark my words, the day may come when your very life will hang on your understanding o' native ways."

At last, after more weeks of hard travel, the brigade reached the place which Mr. Longmore and the chief inland had chosen for the new post—a spot about fifty miles from where the smiling town of Battleford would some day stand. It was the country of the bison, the red deer and the antelope, and to the westward stretched the plains, unmapped and all but unknown.

Here on the north bank of the stream all hands worked at top speed, clearing a site and building the log houses inside a stockade which must protect them during the fast-approaching winter. Once again, in this far land, David heard the wild bugles of the geese ringing down the night. Once again he saw the stockades drifted deep in snow, and for months he was kept busy learning, from Oman and the others, the complicated ritual of Indian barter.

Often, by the firelight, David would set himself exercises in mathematics. In this the chief inland, Mr. Tomison, as well as Mitchell Oman, encouraged him. But study was not easy in the crowded room. There was talk and sometimes, while the blizzard shrilled round the eaves, one of the veteran Scots would feel the memory of home strong upon him. Then would come the wild and haunting music of the pipes, or the room would ring with the rough emotion of the song:

"From the lone shieling of the misty island,
Mountains divide us, and the waste of seas;
But still the blood is strong, the heart is Highland,
And we in dreams behold the Hebrides."

Exiles all, these Scots found comfort in the hope that when their long service ended they could leave this wild land and be with their kith and kin again. The call of Highland glens was strong on nights like these.

But for the charity boy of London slums, there could be no such wistful hope. For what had he to go back to? It made him feel separate and alone to know that, of all of them, he would never be going home. Home? But already this unspoiled, waiting land was beginning to set its mark upon him. Could he not prove himself the sort who could claim this for his own?

It was a strong land which weeded out the weaklings. It was a land where one must succeed or fail according to his own worth.

Then, one night, somewhere within him there seemed to be a voice which whispered: "You must know it, love it, take it, make yourself a part of it, share its hardship and its glory, suffer loneliness and rise to triumph in it. Then you will have a home such as these men can never know—a home which you have built with your own life."

CHAPTER TWELVE

Dᴀᴠɪᴅ Tʜᴏᴍᴘsᴏɴ never spoke
of the heartening sense of his oneness with the North which
had come to him in his loneliness that stormy night. On
several occasions while he was alone with the fatherly Mitchell Oman, he wished he could have found the words. His
superior would not have laughed at such boyish confidences,
that he knew. But in the rough and tumble of a charity
school one learns while very young to keep one's guard up
against the ridicule of elders. So, though that experience
had warmed him strangely, he kept his own confidences
about it.

109

As the months passed, and spring and early summer came again, David found, however, how strongly it was influencing not only his daily life here, but all his dreams of his own future. If this immensity of wilderness was to be his home, it was natural that he should look on it with different eyes than those whose ties to the Old World still held them.

In spite of the company's challenge to the Nor'westers, the trade that spring and summer proved decidedly disappointing. Though they had set up the new post in a country rich in furs, and though the river was a favored water route, only a fraction of the trade which Tomison and Longmore had reason to hope for came their way. It was in mid-September that Mitchell Oman confided to David what the trouble was.

"Yon Nor'westers have outwitted us again," he said. "Here we've set up the post fair in good trapping grounds. But what have the rascals frae Montreal done but open up a new post forty miles upriver frae us. They skimmed the cream o' the trade all spring and now they're out to take even the skim they've left us."

David, who had been tallying the beaver pelts as they went into the fur press, waited while the old trader cut a fill of black twist tobacco and stuffed it into the bowl of his pipe.

"Y'see laddie," Oman continued, "it's no unlike a game o' leapfrog, played halfway across a continent. No matter how far west we come, the Nor'westers keep one jump ahead of us. If ever we're to win, 'tis a bold leap we must be making."

"But leap-frogging much farther—won't that land us among the hostile Blackfeet and the Piegans, out on the open plains?"

Oman ran gnarled fingers through his beard. "Aye. An' fighting tribes they are, the pair o' them. However, oor fine gentlemen in London have little care for that. It's no them will be losing their scalps if trouble comes." Then, perhaps thinking he had been too free with his criticism before an apprentice, the old Scot crammed his bonnet on his head and went out.

Outside, he turned back. "But mind ye, Davvie," he called from the doorway. "Mr. Longmore's no man's fool. He'll be working out a plan."

Waterfowl in unbelievable numbers were gathering in the sloughs, and the poplars were rich in their autumn coloring before David heard what the plan was.

Late one golden afternoon Mr. Longmore called Dave to his quarters.

"Sit down, Thompson," he said quietly. His manner was that of one talking to an equal. "You've seen for yourself how ill the wind blows. The Nor'westers have stolen a march on us again. Mr. Tomison and I have decided to go them one better." Mr. Longmore rose and, clasping his lean hands behind him, began to pace the room slowly.

"How old are you now?" he asked unexpectedly.

"Seventeen, sir."

"I note you've been studying your navigation every chance you get. How would you like to have the opportunity to use it?"

"I'd like that fine, sir," David answered, a bit breathlessly.

Mr. Longmore chewed his scraggy mustache. "You're young for such a mission as the one we have in mind. But who else is there to send?" He stopped before the bench where David sat. "I'm putting you in charge of six men, with orders to make contact with the Blackfeet and the Piegans."

For perhaps a minute he looked down searchingly. "I expect a straight answer, Thompson. Do you believe yourself equal to the task?"

Eager as he was to lead an expedition out across the plains, David was mature enough not to indulge in wishful thinking.

111

Winter would soon swoop, and in that treeless land lean hunting and hungry weeks might lie ahead. The Indians' attitude to the company was an unknown quantity and certainly he would have the cunning, probably the hostility, of the wily Nor'westers to contend with.

"May I say one thing, sir, before I make my answer?"

Mr. Longmore nodded.

"Then it's this, sir. I believe I've learned enough of navigation to lead the party. But plains Indians and their ways are strange to me. I can't honestly promise I'd do well in trade."

Mr. Longmore paused before the small window opening. Beyond him, David could see the poplars on the low bluff across the Saskatchewan. In a short time the tree clumps and the vast grasslands would be stark and desolate under the drifting snow. It was a hazardous time to send a party out, and it was plain that Mr. Longmore knew it.

"This will be more a scouting than a trading venture," he stated. "Our first move must be to establish friendly contact with the plains tribes. Quite apart from the bad name the Nor'westers have likely given us, the Blackfeet and the Piegans will have cause to be suspicious of our motives in pushing westward into their country. They're cocks of the walk now. They intend to remain so."

Then Mr. Longmore explained about the Kootenay tribes. "Until white traders supplied the Blackfeet and the Piegans with firearms, they were no match for the Kootenays, who held the mountain passes and ruled most of the rich buffalo hunting country on the eastern foothills. But the bows and arrows of the Kootenays were useless against the musket. The plains tribes had their revenge and drove them deep into the ranges. Now their fear is that the tables will be reversed, that the Kootenays will get in touch with white traders and provide themselves with firearms in their turn. So, as you value your life, you must do or say nothing which will cause the

112

Blackfeet or the Piegans to suspect you even know the Kootenays so much as exist. They'd never allow a musket to
cross the Rockies, even if it meant slaying the lot of us."

David had been listening thoughtfully. "But sooner or later
we'll have to open up trade with the Kootenays, won't we,
sir?" he asked.

Longmore nodded. "If our company does not, the Nor'-
westers will. If you can bring back information about where
the passes lie, well and good. In fact, should you succeed in
this, your first expedition, it might well be you yourself
would be given that dangerous task. But our immediate purpose is making friendly contact with the Blackfeet and Piegans. Their scouts must know we have entered this country.
Your task will be to convince them that we are their friends.
I think that answers your question." Mr. Longmore paused.
"Well, what's your answer? Want to tackle it?"

"That I do, sir. For look you—"

For the first time during the interview, Mr. Longmore
smiled. The twists of speech peculiar to Highland Scot, to
French-Canadian *voyageur,* half-breed, as well as that of
Englishmen of both high and low degree were familiar to
him. You found them everywhere in the vanguard of the fur
trade. But David Thompson's "look you," as well as the crisp
Welsh inflection which all his life he never quite lost, amused
him somewhat.

"Look you," he mimicked with kindly humor, "are you
saying you are prepared to undertake this mission?"

"Yes, sir," David answered instantly.

And so it was arranged.

It was well into October when David Thompson, with six
chosen men, left Manchester House, as the new post on the
Saskatchewan was now being called. Each was provided with a
horse by the company, and in addition some had bought a

second mount for themselves. Not so their youthful leader. Being still an articled apprentice, he possessed scarcely enough shillings to rub together. Besides, learning always from the Indians, he saw the wisdom of traveling light. However, both for work and for companionship, he decided to take Black Boy along.

"I wouldn't fancy his chances against the hordes of wild Blackfeet curs," Mitchell Oman cautioned. "Best let him bide wi' me, laddie, till your return."

David thanked him and shook his head. "We stick together. Besides, he's a giant among such dogs and knows all the tricks. I've seen him stand off a whole pack of Indian dogs at York." David affectionately regarded the Newfoundland, who stood looking up at him with wise, bright eyes. For days Black Boy had been sensing that some move was afoot and had not let his young master from his sight. "You're coming, never fear," Dave told him.

Black Boy's tail waved excitedly. Then rearing up, tall as a man, he planted his great forepaw on his loved master's shoulders. For a moment they wrestled as David had taught him to do, then, with a brisk slap on the shoulder to say the game was over, David turned, with the dog close at his heels, and entered the storehouse to see the last of the packs made up.

For ten days the party of Indians and French Canadians traveled in a southwesterly direction across the slightly rolling grasslands. Here and there they found good camping places in what, in his diary, David termed "islands" of small poplar. According to his native guides, it was vitally important that they find an ancient landmark known among the tribes as the One Pine. David had checked the bearings of this landmark as carefully as possible from the scanty information available at Manchester House. Now, night after night, while the others rested around the campfire, he would take Black Boy with him to some near-by ridge. Often, too, at high noon, his men would see him busy with strange instruments. They could not know their youthful leader was struggling with his first problems in actual navigation.

It disturbed their unschooled minds to see him vaguely outlined against the night sky on the crest of a ridge, with Black Boy standing guard over him. Why should anyone peer through strange tubes of brass, prying into the secrets of the heavens? To them it smacked of some black magic, and more than once a weary man beside the fire murmured that surely no good would come of it.

For David, riding a horse was a new experience, and this newness was shared by several of his *voyageurs*. On trail, portage or by canoe, they were the equal of any Indian. But during those first days, these inexperienced ones detected amusement at their awkwardness on the faces of their red-skinned companions.

One morning, soon after they had broken camp, David's horse swerved sharply to avoid a badger hole and threw him. Agile as a cat, he took the fall without injury. As he remounted, he saw the Indians chuckling at his mishap.

Paul Poulet, oldest of the *voyageurs,* swung his horse alongside David's as they rode to overtake the others. "Are you going to let these *sauvages* laugh at you?" he demanded.

David grinned. "There's no denying I came a cropper."

"*Moi,* I would soon take the smile off their faces," Poulet declared. "One must never allow these *sauvages* to think themselves as good as a white man."

"But they *are* as good—or better—when it comes to horsemanship."

"No matter," Poulet growled. "You'll find yourself in trouble if you do not keep them in their places. Ruling with a rod of iron. This is important in a leader."

115

David turned in the saddle to face the protesting man. "When I earn their respect, I dare say they will give it."

"*Sacre bleu!* But you have the power to compel it—now."

David stared at him. "Like old Marten, I suppose?"

"I have warned you," Poulet said. "I can do no more. You are a strange one, truly."

However, before the hour was out, Paul Poulet realized that young Thompson possessed some of the qualifications for leadership. Of recent days they had been riding through country foreign to even the Indians. David had had to travel solely by compass, tying in from point to point on the stellar and solar observations he had been making to establish his position on the sketch map he was planning. Now one of the Indians who had been scouting ahead came galloping back to the main party.

"The One Pine lies straight ahead," he reported in wonder.

Poulet's eyes grew wide. "This is good work, *mon vieux!* But how could you tell where that landmark lies when you have never seen it?"

David touched his compass case. "With this—and the stars."

"The signs of the forest I can understand. But this!" Poulet's glance was an odd mixture of doubt and admiration.

Now, as the horses cantered to the crest of the low ridge, it was David's turn to be surprised. Among Indians and traders, the One Pine had become a legend. There was no other pine within a hundred miles, yet there it stood, four feet through the butt, a green giant in this all but treeless land. Only now David saw that the top third of the great tree had been cut away. Crippled and already beginning to die, it was silhouetted grimly against the open sky. What vandalism was this? David Thompson wondered.

He asked the leading Indian about it.

The man's gaze shifted uneasily. He shook his head, but the denial lacked conviction.

"Out with it," David urged. "Anyone can see you know what happened."

"Well, if you must know, a Piegan Indian did it, a few years back, when the smallpox slaughtered us."

Without comment, the white men waited. "He and his family were taken with the sickness," the Indian related. "They camped beneath its branches and the Piegan prayed to the spirit of the mighty pine. His bow and arrows he laid as a sacrifice at its feet. The day before he had offered it his three horses. The sickness was very bad. His oldest son was dying. Soon all the Piegan had to offer was a bowl of water. The One Pine mocked him. It had an evil spirit. It would not save him. The Piegan had a large family but only his wife and one small son did not die. When the Piegan grew strong enough, he took his revenge. He climbed the One Pine and chopped its head off."

A murmur of astonishment came from the superstitious *voyageurs*. "What do you think of that?" Paul Poulet asked David.

"I think the Piegan was foolish," David answered.

Stubbornly, the Indian guide shook his head. "No, the Piegan was wise. As I told you, the tree had an evil spirit."

Such slavish superstition challenged David as even Paul Poulet's criticism of his leadership had failed to do. Ever since he had arrived in the North, three years before, his fearless mind had been appalled by the Indians' enslavement to such beliefs. As he recorded in his diary, fear of the "Metchee Manito," or Evil Spirit, and "Weesarkejauk," the Tempter, was stronger than their belief in the Good Spirit. "A missionary has never been among them," he wrote years later in his *Narrative*, "and my knowledge of their language

117

has not enabled me to do more than teach the unity of God."

But even now, for all a youth's reluctance to speak of his beliefs, he longed to strike the shackles of demon worship from these native minds.

"Listen," he said, "if your people worship the Good Spirit only, the Metchee Manito can have no power over you. For I believe—"

The Indian, sitting bolt upright on his pony, raised a warning hand. "You make bad talk. You have defied the power of Metchee Manito. Punishment will follow."

"And I will keep defying him," David stated boldly.

Half-angry, half-afraid, the Indian pressed his hands against his ears. "Evil will come of this," he warned. Then wheeling his mount, he and his comrades galloped from under the shadow of the brooding tree, as if by doing so they were proving to its listening spirit that they, at least, had had no part in their leader's defiance.

CHAPTER THIRTEEN

"You see," Paul Poulet commented darkly as the party rode on, "he has no liking for your reckless talk."

"But it's the truth."

"'T is all very well for missionaries to speak like that," the *voyageur* said with a shrug. "But we are traders and must tread softly. And truly, young one, you must comprehend by now that you have trespassed on dangerous ground. The truth, is it? Me, I am a trader and value my own scalp. So the truth I understand is whatever manner of speaking will smooth our way for us."

David was troubled. "But all I did was try to reason with them—"

"Does one reason with cattle?" Poulet broke in.

"What way is that to talk?" David demanded heatedly.

The other's black eyebrows arched knowingly. "Consider the depraved, savage life they lead! How can one look on them as fully human?"

David's thoughts flashed back to Young Otter, the Indian hunter, and his family at York, and to others who, in their primitive way, had shown him friendship and hospitality. "Every bit as human as ourselves," he declared.

"There have been priests of our religion who spoke like that," the *voyageur* pointed out. "They went out to live with them. Perhaps you have not heard the names of our holy fathers who were fiendishly tortured by these very people they wanted only to befriend?"

"As to that, I have no certain knowledge." But David felt himself on the defensive now.

"There was Father Lalemont and Father Brebeuf, to name but two."

"The history of New France is not taught in English schools."

"How lamentable," Poulet commented tartly. "Who knows but that in days to come it might have saved the life of at least one young apprentice of the English company." With that parting shot, Paul Poulet's moccasined heels thumped his pony's ribs and he cantered off.

Glancing down, David's eyes met those of Black Boy who, after chasing a rabbit through the poplar grove beneath One Pine, was trotting at the flank of his master's horse. "In their wigwams they have been good to me, just as they were good to you, old fellow," he said aloud.

The rest of that morning, as he rode alone, David blamed himself for having allowed his second-in-command to reduce the argument between them to one of smart trading, then later of white superiority. If you took at its face value what the Bible taught, then all men were brothers, no matter what the color of their skins. But quite apart from his great religious belief, David Thompson was by nature one of those who, both in science and in the world of men, must follow the truth for its own sake, no matter where it leads them. At times such acceptance of facts as facts led him into trouble. The worldly-wise were inclined to consider you a simpleton if you refused to judge the right and wrong by what you yourself got out of it.

In some respects it called to mind the struggle he had experienced the previous winter with his navigation exercises. There, approximations and guessing simply were not good enough. Exact truth, no matter how awkward its fractions and repeating decimals, must be discovered and acted upon. It was folly to try and make yourself believe what your common sense told you could not be so.

So it was with what he had said to the Indian about his fear of evil spirits. Poulet might call it dangerous talk. But without stooping to deception, how, David asked himself, could he have spoken otherwise?

For twenty-three days the little party rode westward, seeking, without success, for signs of an Indian encampment and finding no food except now and then an old buffalo bull whose flesh was so stringy and poor it gave no nourishment. Black Boy was a good hunter but had been able to run down so few rabbits and small game that his ribs were showing. The Indians of the party were ominously silent about this scarcity of meat, and at times when David tried to question them they avoided answering and moved away. Not until the party was south of the Bow River did they reveal where they believed the blame lay.

In a good year, this rich grazing country should be covered with the herds which wintered near the foothills where the seasonal "Chinook" winds decreased the depth of snow. Old hunters at Manchester House had assured David meat would be abundant there, but no game larger than the occasional antelope was sighted. That evening, for the first time, the Indians declined to share the common fire. Instead, they picketed their horses apart and withdrew to a fire of buffalo chips a quarter of a mile away from the whites.

The bitter wind grew stronger, and after dark dry snow swirled over the huddled figures. Then, in the November darkness, there came the echoes of drumbeats and of Indian chanting. The *voyageurs* glanced uneasily at one another. The wind shrilled eerily through the dead grass tufts, fanning the embers of their fire into flame and casting swaying shadows over the weathered faces of the men.

Poulet drew his buffalo robe closer and cleared his throat. "Myself, I think it makes bad blood to interfere in the religious beliefs of others, even the beliefs of a *sauvage*," he remarked to no one in particular.

A man across the fire nodded in surly agreement. "No buffalo in a place where we should have found the best of hunting. The devil is in it, surely."

"But yes," Poulet replied. Now, for the first time, he looked straight at David Thompson. "Explain away our ill luck, if you can, my friend."

David shook his head. "I can't explain it."

Poulet stirred the fire. "At least you are being truthful in admitting—"

"But this I know," David asserted. "There is some reason which makes sense. The whims of so-called evil spirits have nothing to do with it."

"Bold talk that, for one so young," a man muttered. There, on the unmapped plains and with a blizzard threatening, these unlettered men were far from confident that the disappearance of the herds had not been inflicted on them by black magic of some sort.

David realized that he was face to face with a crisis—the first real test of his fitness for leadership. It was evident that the Indians believed he had angered the Metchee Manito and that, if they were to escape its evil spell, they must shun him. The *voyageurs,* too, were wondering. One wrong move now and their inexperienced leader would have mutiny or desertion on his hands. And without the Indians' help, 'the situation was hopeless.

David threw off the robe he had drawn around him and sprang to his feet. "I'm going to find out what mischief is in the making," he said. Black Boy rose, stretched and eyed his master expectantly. Then, while the white men looked at one another and shook their heads, the youth and his dog faced the biting wind and headed through the blackness toward the Indian camp.

The rhythm of drumbeats quickened as David drew nearer to the Indians' fire. He halted close by, hidden in the darkness. Black Boy pressed against his knees. David felt for the Newfoundland's head and stroked it. Amid all this doubt and suspicion, here was one who trusted him.

"Be kind to us, be kind to us, O Metchee Manito," rose the guttural chant. "Be kind to us and send the buffalo that we may live."

The pitiable fear in the voices smote David to the heart. In spite of Poulet's ridicule, in spite of the exploitation and degradation they were subjected to around the forts, he saw these people not as debased savages but as his own brothers in the sight of God. Later, in his *Narrative,* he was to write: "Christianity alone can eradicate these sad superstitions, and who will teach them?"

"O, Metchee Manito, torture us no longer." The chant rose stronger now against the drone of the gale.

"Stay close, Boy," David whispered. Then he walked into the circle of firelight and sat down among his frightened Indian comrades.

The next morning, when the party rode again, the Indians rode with them. They had admitted around their fire that they believed the Metchee Manito had driven the buffalo away. And this curse had come, they said, because their leader had challenged Metchee Manito back there at the One Pine.

"What you should have done last night is use their superstition to your own advantage," Paul Poulet insisted as they rode side by side with Dave that bitter morning. "You should trade on it—spin them some story to make them think you have the evil one on your side. I've seen that done more than once by old traders. And it works, my boy. It works!"

David did not answer.

"I've been telling you all along you have to trick an Indian. It's foolish to argue. They are not as you and I, my boy. They are not reasonable beings."

"But doesn't that backfire sooner or later? Once an Indian finds out you have tricked him, how can he trust you again?"

"The proof of the pudding is in the eating. Our Indians are on the verge of desertion. And there, *mon vieux,* you have your answer."

To every leader worthy of the name come times of loneliness and haunting doubt; times when all that stands between him and utter failure is a desperate loyalty to the faith within. Such a time came to David Thompson during those days of travel over the wintry plains south of the Bow. Even among the whites of his party there were some who came out openly for turning back. Paul Poulet, to his everlasting credit, was not one of them. But supplies were exhausted, winter had come, and to be caught far out on these treeless grasslands would be to perish.

Yet David pressed on. In such a situation many an older explorer would have done the same. With some, it might have been because of bravado, or pride, or sheer desperation. With David Thompson it was none of these, for the fact was that he alone of all the party did not believe in the whims and workings of blind chance. These others suspected the party had become lost. David, with his mathematical turn of mind, knew that sextant and compass and sun and stars do not lie. Guessing allows the thin edge of doubt to enter. Thanks to his almost daily observations for latitude and longitude, David did not need to guess. He *knew*. He had set his course and would follow it. To him the notion that they were lost was as far-fetched as was his Indians' belief that Metchee Manito was having his revenge on them.

Strung out on their shaggy ponies, shielding their faces against the cutting wind, the dispirited *voyageurs* and Indians were trailing their leader one noon when suddenly a shout went up. Reining in, they saw a cluster of tiny "v"s miles away on the horizon. An hour later, Kootanae Appee, the six-foot-six war chief of the Piegans, rode out with his warriors to welcome them!

For weeks David was an honored guest of the war chief and of Saukamappee, a wise old leader whose stories of wars and hunting went back well over fifty years. Lounging around the wigwam fire, David heard much of Indian warfare before the days of firearms; of the new power which the capture of horses from the Spaniards gave to the Blackfeet and kindred tribes; of the terrible ravages of smallpox in 1781, and how the white man's weapons turned the tables

125

in favor of whatever tribe was fortunate enough to possess them.

"I am told that with such weapons your people were able to drive the Kootenay people back into the mountains," David commented one evening as he sat with the old chief and Kootanae Appee on the buffalo robes beside the latter's fire.

"The Kootenays are a brave people," the war chief answered. "But against our firearms their bows and arrows are not enough. Yes, we did drive them into the mountains." His piercing glance rested on the white youth. "And we will keep them there."

Old Saukamappee leaned forward and prodded David's knee with a gnarled forefinger. "Your talk has been straight —so far. May it still be so." He and the war chief looked at one another. "We believe you when you say you were sent to make friends with us and to ask us to come to your post to trade. Now tell us this. Were you not also sent to find out our secret of where the mountain passes are?"

David knew he could not evade that question. He must either lie or speak the truth. What he did not know was that native scouts in the hire of the rival Nor'westers had, for weeks, been shadowing his party, and that during most of that time the Piegans had been kept informed of all his movements. Not only that, but the shrewd Nor'westers, suspecting that behind this Hudson's Bay venture was the same desire they themselves entertained, had told Kootanae Appee that the Hudson's Bay people had come to open trade with the Kootenays.

Inexperienced he might be, but during his stay with these people David had learned they possessed native intelligence of a high order. They were quick to detect—and resent— attemps at double-dealing. And anyway, he was no hand at

126

intrigue. Now he realized his whole future with these people lay in a straight answer.

Slowly, choosing his words with great care, he related exactly what Mr. Longmore had said to him at parting. A studied silence on the part of the two chiefs followed.

Then Kootenae Appee spoke. "Your words ring true. We believe what you say. You were sent first to make friends with us and to ask us to come to the Saskatchewan to trade with you, instead of with the Nor'westers. We also believe the other thing you have just told us—that your company would like to know what passes will lead them into the Kootenay country. But that is our secret. It will remain so."

"It is not that we do not trust you," Saukamappee explained. "We know now you talk straight. But you traders are all the same. For furs you would give our enemies firearms. This must never be."

"I am glad you believe we are your friends," David said.

The war chief nodded. "Long may you remain so. But if you arm the Kootenays, we must fight you. Say no more about the passes."

CHAPTER FOURTEEN

BUT EVEN AFTER the talk turned to other matters, David kept thinking of the mountain passes and wondering about the country beyond. This was years before Alexander Mackenzie, the bold Nor'wester who would be the first man to reach the Pacific from Canada by land, had penetrated the Rockies. Tonight as, chin on knees, David gazed wide-eyed into the embers of the fire in the chief's lodge, he asked himself how long it must be before he would be able to make that dangerous journey into the unknown.

For as surely as he sat there someone was bound to open up those carefully guarded passes. Already, in the few years since he had left London, he had seen a country larger than all of Europe. On the seas, Captain Cook and other famous navigators were widening the horizons for all mankind. Why should someone not do the same for this rich and waiting land?

Not that he could not see the Piegans' reasons for wanting to keep explorers out. Once the passes were penetrated, their supremacy would be threatened. You could not condemn them on that count. Was not his own company acting with much the same motives in trying to thwart the Colonial Office's desire to have the Hudson's Bay country accurately mapped? Both Piegan and English trader were determined to exploit their secret knowledge for their narrow, personal advantage. Neither would surrender those secrets without a fight.

And yet David Thompson, with his Welsh instinct for freedom, believed this great land should be open to all with the daring and skill to possess it. But before the hungry and the poor of Europe could enter it, the territory must be explored and accurately mapped.

And while the two chiefs talked of great hunts and tribal wars, memory took David back to the Gray Coat School and the day the headmaster had promised him a future as a surveyor with the company. Seven years' apprenticeship and the art of navigation would be mastered!

But under Governor Hearne and the bully Marten, his navigation had remained at the elementary stage. The months and years were passing. Was he never to be more than a trader in furs? He had seen enough to know how ambitions were killed and spirits broken by the routine of the forts. Was this what the future held for him?

And yet Mr. Longmore and the chief inland had encouraged him to believe he could learn. His trails had run true on this journey. His navigation, though rudimentary, had been accurate. Now that the company was fighting the Nor'westers for supremacy on the plains, a man who could travel by the stars and sun need not always remain a menial.

A thorough mastery of surveying and navigation—these were the keys to this great land and to his own success. If he could complete this first expedition without disaster, it would be a good start. But how much there was for him still to learn! And in the wilderness, who was there to teach him?

Weeks later, as he guided his party safely back across the plains to Manchester House, David Thompson thought with some concern of the reception awaiting him. His orders had been to establish friendly relations with the Piegans. In that he had succeeded. But he had also been told to induce them to come to Manchester House to trade. And in that he had completely failed.

The very afternoon of his return, David appeared before Mr. Longmore and Mitchell Oman. He gave his report in direct, clear-cut sentences.

Well-disposed toward David though he was, Mr. Longmore could not hide his disappointment. "Well, Oman, what say you to all this?" he asked.

The veteran trader twirled his bonnet thoughtfully. "He gives us the bitter wi' the sweet, at ony rate," he commented. "Some in his boots would be pullin' the wool o'er oor eyes about the Piegans coming. But the lad comes right out wi' the unpleasant truth."

Mr. Longmore nodded slowly. "But could you not have offered compelling inducements? You know we here would have gone to great lengths to have the Piegans transfer their trade from the Nor'westers to us."

"The chiefs, sir, see no good reason why they should risk the longer journey to this post just to please us. They say the Nor'westers have always used them fairly."

Mitchell Oman stroked his immense and grizzled beard. "Tell us, lad, what's the country like yonder? And aboot yon mountain passes—?"

"One moment," Mr. Longmore interrupted. "Turnor will want to hear this." He crossed the room and knocked on the inner door.

A lean, scholarly man entered.

"Mr. Turnor, this is David Thompson, the apprentice I was telling you about," Longmore explained.

The distinguished-looking stranger acknowledged the introduction with a formal nod, then stood by the window, his hands clasped behind him, his close-cropped head tilted attentively.

"I was asking aboot the passes, sir," Oman explained. "Some day the company must force them, for if we don't, yon Alex Mackenzie or some other of the Nor'west partners will. They're hard-drivin', determined men. There's bound to be rich trade beyond the mountains. If only we knew where best to seek them—"

"Tell me, boy," the stranger inquired, "how far up the Bow River were you able to penetrate? And do you think the headwaters of that stream might provide a route through the Rockies?"

"It's a possibility, sir," David answered, "but the war chief allowed me no chance to explore west of their encampment. I had my telescope, though, and on several clear days I could sight the river's course well up into the foothills. And I took these compass bearings from a known base line I managed to pace out." Here David opened his buckskin jacket, produced his well-thumbed notebook and laid it on the table.

The stranger reached for it. "May I?"

"By all means," Mr. Longmore urged. "We are eager to hear what you make of it."

As he turned the pages, a change came over the stranger's

face and something of the tiredness went from his searching eyes. "Do you mind if I take these notes to my quarters and study them more closely?" he asked Longmore. He regarded David with new interest. "It's possible this is the very lad I need."

As Mr. Turnor left the room, Mitchell Oman seemed as proud as if David were his own son. "D'ye ken who the stranger is, laddie?" he whispered hoarsely. "He's none other than Philip Turnor—"

"Not *the* Philip Turnor? Not the one who compiled the *Nautical Almanac* we studied back at school?"

"The very same," Mr. Longmore answered. "As you doubtless heard at York Factory, the Colonial Office has been urging the company to map its territory. There were evasions until, at last, the government grew tired of the governors' excuses. So Mr. Turnor has been sent out as astronomer and surveyor. And what a colossal task for one lone man—and he no longer young!"

All this was so astounding that David wondered if his senses had tricked him. Had Mr. Turnor really said those words— "the very lad I need"?

"If he decides to train you, 'twill mean a long, hard grind," Mr. Longmore was reminding him. "No need to tell you how shorthanded we are here. And it will take months before I can receive authority from Mr. Colen to relieve you of your regular duties. However, it is only fair to tell you that Mr. Turnor himself has authority from the company to choose any capable apprentice he finds, and to train him so he can take over the mapping and surveying in later years."

David's eyes were shining. He felt like one who has been wandering uncertainly through lowland fog and who suddenly comes out on some sunlighted hill and sees the long trail ahead, arduous, but clearly defined.

As soon as the evening meal was over, Philip Turnor sent for David and gave him a test in penmanship and calculation.

"H'mm," Mr. Turner said. "Not bad, not bad at all. You have much to learn, but I can see you have at least a grasp of fundamentals. I shall be setting out for the Athabasca in a month or so. I need an assistant, and what better way to learn a craft than by practicing it? I have spoken to Mr. Longmore and he is willing to assume the responsibility of allowing you to come, pending formal permission from Factor Colen. Will you join me?"

"Oh, Mr. Turnor, sir—" But for the moment David was too overcome to speak his gratitude.

Mr. Turnor smiled. "I think you'll do. At least you have the will to learn. Tonight I will be taking a lunar observation. Shall we use that as our first lesson? So if you will meet me outside the west gate, just before midnight—"

A few moments later, when David left the great surveyor, he changed his mind about returning to the guardroom. He had come to another turning-point in his life and for the time being he wanted to be alone, to sort out and appraise the many thoughts which kept flashing through his mind. In the staff quarters there would be interruptions and incessant talk. The others would want to hear the details of his journey westward. Ten minutes ago he had been looking forward to such a sociable evening after weeks on the trail. He still was, but first he must take a walk alone to—as he put it—"get his feet back on the ground."

Once outside the stockade, David strolled along the well-worn path skirting the swift Saskatchewan. Black Boy stalked proudly ahead, pausing now and then to glance back, making sure his master was following. Across the river, the birches showed soft and silvery in the failing light. They brought to mind an old Welsh song David used to hear his mother sing as she plied the shuttle of her loom:

"The ash grove how graceful, how plainly 'tis speaking,
The harp through it playing has language for me;
Whenever the light through its branches is breaking,
A host of kind faces is gazing at me.
The friends of my childhood again are before me. . . ."

He was thinking, as he had thought so often during these last three years, of his mother and the hope they shared that he could win a place in the New World and ease the hard lot for the little family. Now, thanks to Mr. Turnor, this hope shone brighter than ever before. To fix the location of the Athabasca and so discover, for the Colonial Office, whether Captain Cook or Mr. Pond was right! To be chosen as assistant for an exploration which could change the future of a nation and a continent!

"Black boy, old fellow!" he exclaimed. "It's come! It's come at last." The big Newfoundland reared, planting his great paws on his master's shoulders, his tongue lolling, his mouth grinning with delight. "You can carry a load, Boy. Mr. Turnor will want you, too. I know he will."

Spring had advanced swiftly these last days, and the river bend below was already free of ice. As the two walked on, they heard the chatter of native children, playing below the melting cut-bank. Suddenly David heard the rumble of falling rock, and then a scream.

With Black Boy at his heels, he leaped to the water's edge and sprinted around the bend. A small boy was struggling to free his legs from the fallen clay and stones. The other children, who had run away in alarm, were coming back and David was helping the boy to his feet, when Black Boy barked a sharp warning.

But although David heard the clatter of falling stones, the warning came too late. As he whirled, he saw tons of clay and boulders racing toward him. There was only time to give the boy a push, to see Black Boy drag him clear. David rolled madly to one side, but not before a stone weighing several hundredweight had crashed against his thigh. Stunned and helpless, he was dimly aware of tons of rubble charging toward him. Then Black Boy had him by the shoulder and was tugging at him.

After the Indian children had run for help and David had been carried on a litter into the fort, Mitchell Oman made ready to set the broken leg. The boy's senses were fogged by pain but just outside the circle of candlelight, he imagined he glimpsed the faces of Mr. Longmore and Philip Turnor. Now things were turning dark again.

" 'Twill hurt, ye sore, laddie," Mitchell Oman cautioned. His voice seemed to come from far away. "So grit yer teeth. Ready?"

David could not speak, but his eyes gave the signal. He gripped the poplar poles of the bunk until his knuckles showed white. His lips were compressed and beads of sweat glinted on his face in the candlelight as Oman set the bone and bound on the freshly hewn splint. Mercifully, the stab of pain proved its own anesthetic and when David's senses cleared, the room was empty except for the old Scot, who sat like a burly statue on the bench beside him.

"How long must I lie here?" David asked presently.

"Na, laddie, why fret yourself?" Mitchell Oman soothed. " 'Tis a mishap, I'll grant. But such things happen to the best o' us."

"Please, Mitchell, tell me." This was the first time David had called his superior by his first name, and it was plain the old Scot liked it. But when Oman said "a month or two," David turned his face to the log wall to hide the tears of disappointment starting in his eyes.

"A fine, long rest ye'll be having, ye rascal—and wi' the

spring work coming on," Oman jested. He rose and stood looking down, his steel-gray eyes warm with pity. "Shall I dowse the candle, Davvie?" he asked gently.

David nodded mutely. He heard the moccasined feet move across the clay floor, the door closed softly and he was alone. "A fine, long rest!" David thought in anguish. He knew he would not be traveling with Philip Turnor now. His great chance had come—and gone.

Difficulties and reverses, so long as they were coupled with action—these he could face. But for a youth of his boundless energy, this helpless waiting seemed more than could be borne.

A knock interrupted his dark thoughts and Mr. Turnor, lantern in hand, came in. He carried something in a leather case. "Mitchell suggested I come tonight," he explained.

"Thank you, sir," David managed. But he did not understand.

Mr. Turnor went directly to the point. "How badly do you desire to learn what I can teach you?"

David swallowed hard. "More than I ever wanted anything." And then because of the disappointment and the pain and the weakness, the barriers of reserve and youthful pride came down. "Oh, sir!" he went on, his voice choked with a yearning passion, "I don't want to be just a trader—or a clerk cooped up within four walls. I want to find out things—to see, to know—to really *know*—"

"Go on," Mr. Turnor urged quietly. Shrewd judge of human nature that he was, he knew that in this shadowy room he was hearing a confession which this fatherless boy had never revealed to anyone in the fort. "What is it makes you want to *know*?"

"I can't explain, sir. I haven't the words. But when a person's ignorant, he's like in a prison. I want to be free—in my body, but in my mind most of all. I want to understand."

In desperation, the pent-up hopes found the channel of

136

words. It was seldom enough, Philip Turnor thought, that one finds a boy with the desire for knowledge, for knowledge's sake. Yet here, defying circumstance, was one hungering for it. Ignorance was indeed a prison, but here was one who would never cease beating at its bars.

"Well, David, all this is pretty much what I've come about," he said presently, opening the instrument case. "See this large, ten-inch sextant? In brass, by the famous Dollard. There's none better made. I want you to have it—now."

David stared. This was not the first time his senses had played tricks on him tonight.

"I quite realize you don't know its full use yet. But you will, my boy, you will. I have been examining your notes of your Piegan journey and I believe you have the makings of a good surveyor. What struck me most of all is that you don't approximate—none of this slipshod guessing. And when you don't know a fact, you say so. Here." And with that he placed the sextant in David's hands.

With something like awe, David held it to the lantern light. With such a tool and the understanding to use it, a man could spread the wilderness before him like an open book. No more traveling by dead reckoning, or following crude sketches and Indian rumor about the trails and waterways.

"As I was saying, I've been studying your notes," Mr. Turnor was continuing. "Your ground work is excellent. It will be a few weeks yet before the rivers to the north are open for summer travel and during that time I can teach you much. That is, unless your leg gives you too much pain."

"It won't, sir—I promise you it won't!" David hesitated. "I wish I had some way to thank you—"

"You can thank me by doing honest work," the surveyor said as he rose to leave. "That, in the field of mapping, seems something of a rarity hereabouts—judging by the errors and slipshod guessing about the Athabasca so popularized by that trader, Peter Pond. I admire a man who'll follow truth, no matter where it leads him." Mr. Turnor laid his hand on David's arm. "I may be wrong, but somehow I believe you're of the breed who will."

In spite of the hurt in his leg David Thompson slept soundly. He was not aware, until he opened his eyes the next morning, that he had slept the night through, holding the priceless Dollard sextant in his arms.

CHAPTER FIFTEEN

By the time the poplars were in leaf and the rolling grasslands around Manchester House carpeted with new green, David had progressed far enough to know that by hard study and regular practice in what he had already learned, he could master the science on which his heart was set, and on which his future depended. Mr. Turnor was a demanding instructor and when the rivers and lakes to the north were open for water travel, he assured David that neither of them had been wasting their time. "I trust this is only the beginning," he said.

"Mr. Longmore thinks you may be posted to York Factory

next winter, Dave," Mr. Turnor revealed when the day for parting came. "I wish, perhaps as strongly as you do, that you were making the Athabasca exploration with me this summer. But I'm leaving you with enough exercises and texts to occupy your spare time all summer. I expect to winter at York, where I'll be working up my observations and field notes and getting my Athabasca map in final form to submit to those in authority in London. I intend to ask Mr. Colen to assign you to help me with that work."

David had been trying not to think of the opportunities he would miss that summer by being left at Manchester House. And though he had not succeeded, this news did take some of the sting from that disappointment.

"It should prove useful training for you. And since my eyes aren't what they were for the fine work of drafting, this will be a profitable arrangement for both of us." Mr. Turnor held out his hand. "So, Dave, until the snow flies and we meet again—"

David gripped the hand of his distinguished sponsor. "Winter can't come soon enough for me. And thanks again, Mr. Turnor, for everything."

The weeks passed swiftly. By mid-July, with the aid of a stick, David was hobbling about the post and doing light duty. By August he was allowed to lead minor buffalo-hunting parties and go up-river to the wood-cutting camp. By the time the wild fowl were beginning to migrate, he had grown as strong as ever. But by then, too, it was apparent that his leg had been improperly set. For the rest of his days he would travel with a noticeable, though not serious, limp.

After weeks of being confined to his bunk, his zest for activity returned stronger than ever. To compensate for the handicap of his limp, he set himself to learning trick riding from the Indians. He swam and dived in the cold water, and at the wood camp swung an axe with the best of them.

Black Boy swam with him, coursed the plains with him, hunted, worked and slept close to him. Even at night when David would take his precious sextant and climb a small butte behind the post to do the practical work in stellar observation which Mr. Turnor had set for him, the loyal Newfoundland was at his master's side. The *voyageurs* began to call him "Thompson's Shadow."

In late August, when the chief inland's fur brigade returned from Hudson's Bay, the dispatches confirmed what Mr. Turnor had said. David Thompson was posted to York for the coming winter. A few days later, in company with two packet Indians, he and Black Boy began the long water journey eastward, and in due time arrived at York Factory.

David found that great changes had taken place at this famous establishment since old Marten had been superseded by the suave and businesslike Factor Colen. Instead of the bullying and searing broadsides of man-o'-war profanity which David had known during his term of service there, affairs were now conducted with quiet efficiency. In fact, after his weeks of hard paddling, harder portaging and dusk-to-dawn camps, David found York Factory a pleasant place indeed and looked forward to his winter there under Mr. Turnor's tutelage with keen anticipation.

"Old Marten's recall to London is indeed something to be thankful for," David remarked during his first free evening with Jack Jennings and Alf Robinson.

"In some ways, yes," the cautious-spoken Alf commented.

Naturally, David found this lack of enthusiasm for the change in factors surprising. "Hold on now!" he exclaimed. "What's in the wind? You know we three thought Mr. Colen a good master when he was assistant here."

"With old Marten to take the wind out of his sails now and then, he was," Jack drawled. He was the same old, easygoing Jack. The routine of fort life obviously agreed with him and though, by contrast to David's tanned face and lean, supple

141

shoulders, some might term him flabby, he had acquired an air of worldly-wise sophistication which impressed his fellow apprentice, freshly arrived from the raw and strenuous life far inland.

David, more than ever puzzled, asked him what he meant.

"The fact of the matter is, my laddie-buck, that his new authority has gone to Colen's head. Amiable and pleasant-spoken —that I grant you. But only so long as things are going his way."

"Joseph Colen's trouble is that he's too confoundedly ambitious," Alf explained. "He's not like old Marten. He doesn't blast and storm at those who cross him. The head-on attack is not his way. But as clerks, Jack and I see things others don't. Mr. Colen has become so jealous of the factor up at Churchill. And recently, too, of the progress which the chief inland has been making—"

"Not to mention his downright hostility to this surveyor chap, this Philip Turnor—"

"Philip Turnor?" David burst out. "What has Philip Turnor ever done to him? I can't understand that."

"I can," Jennings said. "Colen has a long head on him. He has no stomach for this westward exploration which seems now to have become all the fashion. He hates to see Mr. Turnor and others getting credit in London for such work. Furs are all he cares about."

"Furs—and the further promotion of Joseph Colen," Alf corrected. "Why if I told you—"

"Stow it," Jack broke in guardedly as footsteps sounded in the doorway.

Alf glanced around nervously. Both he and Jack seemed relieved to find that their visitor was only Malcolm Ross, a rawboned young Highlander and one of the new junior officers David had met for the first time that afternoon.

"Come along, Thompson," Ross called from the doorway. "The factor's sent for us."

"Now what?" David thought as, straightening his jacket, he followed the young man outside. "Had I known this was coming, I should have borrowed a razor and hacked off this month-old growth of beard."

The tall, black-haired Ross glanced down and laughed good-naturedly. "Man alive! So you call that tuft of fuzz a beard!"

David's inability to sprout really imposing whiskers was a point on which he was unduly sensitive. He was eighteen now and, though Mitchell Oman had once assured him that "by the time you're my age ye'll have had your fill o' being Esau, the hairy one," he secretly admired the really imposing beards which juniors his age seemed able to grow at will.

As they crossed the yard both knew, however, that this was no time for raillery. "Like as not you've yet to hear of the stir Mr. Turnor's report of last season has caused in London," Ross went on. "All eyes are now on the Athabasca and, the way I hear it, Factor Colen has been instructed by the governors to send an expedition to winter in that region. The country's rich, and it's us or the Nor'westers. My own guess is that this undertaking is already as good as ours." He looked at David appraisingly. "What say you to that prospect?"

David found it difficult to answer. He had been looking forward to wintering here with Mr. Turnor. On the other hand, Alf's and Jack's hint of Joseph Colen's jealousy now threatened all that, for only on the consent of the factor could he be assigned to help Mr. Turnor with his final Athabasca report. "I'm still counting on wintering here," David answered finally. "But if that's not to be, nothing would suit me better than the Athabasca." It might even happen, he thought, that when Mr. Turnor got wind of the chill reception awaiting him here, he might elect to pass the winter at the Athabasca post the factor probably wanted them to set up. That would be ideal, for there, deep in the wilderness, they would be their own masters.

It was obvious from the start, however, that Mr. Colen held quite different ideas.

After greeting them courteously and commenting on how David was filling out, he had a servant draw up chairs for them and, chatting as if they were almost his equals, he discussed in a general way the prospects of the fur trade. He said how regrettable it was that, in spite of all their efforts—his as well as those of the chief inland—the return of furs from Manchester House had been so disappointing.

David ventured to remark that the aggressive policy of the Nor'westers was, in part at least, responsible.

Surprisingly enough, Mr. Colen entirely agreed with this. "My own view—and one I have made after careful study—is that our Manchester House venture simply proves the danger of over-reaching. Like it or no, the Nor'westers are in the trade to stay. A bird in the hand is worth two in the bush, you know. Consolidation, working methodically from a well-established base—this must be our policy from now on." The factor leaned back and spread his thin hands in a gesture of inquiry. "Does not this sound reasonable to you, young gentlemen?"

Neither Ross nor Thompson knew quite what to say.

Then Mr. Colen came to the point. "This is the first day of September. In these latitudes, time is growing short. Five days hence you two will leave for a winter in our own Muskrat Country."

David saw Ross's long jaw clench. The Muskrat Country! That dreary expanse of lakes and muskeg west and south of Hudson's Bay—a trapped-out land which for decades had yielded so poor a harvest of furs that the Nor'westers, and even the occasional unscrupulous free traders, did not deign to dispute the company's control of it!

"Canoes and stores are ready," Mr. Colen was explaining smoothly.

The fiery young Scot's chin went up. "But what about the Athabasca, sir? After Mr. Turnor's fine start, you surely do not intend to surrender it to the Nor'westers?"

Mr. Colin drew in his lips. His full cheeks paled. But when he spoke his voice was controlled—too controlled, so David thought.

"I beg to remind you, Ross, that we just now went into all that. For what, in heaven's name, is the sense of scurrying hither and yon—north to the Athabasca and beyond, westward to the mountains—only to find ourselves a jump behind the rascals from Montreal? Can you wonder that our shipments to London have been falling off? But if you two will back me loyally this winter—"

"Allow me to remind you, sir," Malcolm blurted out, "that when London learns you have scorned to take advantage of Mr. Turnor's hard-won surveys, there'll be some awkward questions asked."

"So?" the factor demanded. Now the mask was off and he was so furious that his prominent eyes almost started from his head. "Are you refusing duty? Is this mutiny?"

The young Highlander shook his head. "Indeed not. I've had my orders and, like it or no, I shall obey them. But I know there will be trouble and I intend to make my own position clear. As for Thompson here—"

"Let Thompson speak for himself," Colen snapped exultantly. The crisis was over and he had won. "Thompson is not one to speak before he thinks." Colen bowed slightly, and with a hint of mockery. "Now, *Mister* Thompson, have you anything to say?" He knew that the Welsh youth was several years younger than his companion. With his round face, snub nose and oddly-cut hair, he was not an imposing figure. Yet he possessed a baffling air of self-reliance and a simple directness which indicated that, should trouble come, he might be the one to lead it.

145

"Only this, sir," David answered. "I have your orders. I will obey them. But my last two seasons in the Far West have opened my eyes. Compared to it, the Hudson's Bay country seems poor indeed. I share the chief inland's and Mr. Turnor's belief that our company has a great future there. Mr. Turnor is doing grand work yonder—"

"Stick to the point, please," the factor interjected, as if such praise of Philip Turnor were distasteful to him.

"I am sticking to the point," David maintained doggedly.

"Which is?"

"That I would be of more use helping Mr. Turnor with his Athabasca surveys than putting in the winter in the Muskrat Country."

Such measured criticism was too much. The factor, for once, completely lost his temper. Here was an underling advocating the very policies he was determined to stamp out. He smote the table. "So you, too, aspire to be one of those so-called trail blazers, do you?" he sneered. He leveled a warning finger. "If you are as wise as I think, you will forget all such notions here and now. Turnor and his pretty maps! I want none of them, and if he but knew it, there are some highly-placed of our governors in London who share my view. Do you think us fools? For why, in the name of common sense, should we publish maps so that the riff-raff of all Europe can come here and dispute possession with us? Never forget this, Thompson—and you, Ross, as well. This is our country. Our private domain—and ours alone. We intend to keep it so."

Then the factor drew out a drawer and handed each of them a parchment. "Here are your marching orders. Having them thus in writing should avoid mistakes, or shall we say—evasion?" He turned to David. "Mr. William Cook will be your assistant. He is waiting now to help you package and load your stores."

146

CHAPTER SIXTEEN

So, WITH A CAREER of scientific
discovery almost within his grasp, David Thompson found
himself thrust a second time into the advance guard in the
fight for furs. Last winter's expedition had had the same motive, but in it there was the lure of discovery and the knowledge that he was being trusted with a dangerous journey
into the Piegan country. But this!

The Muskrat Country! There was contempt in the name
which generations ago had been given to that dismal area
west and south of the Bay—so much contempt that to be

sent there was the next thing to banishment. Whether Sam had found his way through it, or whether he was still in hiding there, he would never need fear detection. No party of any strength had been sent in there for years. And the bold Nor'westers, who were not the men to overlook a profitable trading area, even when it meant clashes with the long-established Hudson's Bay Company, also considered it beneath their notice. Only outlaw traders did business there. It was dubious land in many ways.

At the thought of outlaw traders, another anxiety sprang to David's mind. What if poor Sam had never been able to get farther south? What if, going from bad to worse, he had been driven to becoming one of those outlaw traders and grog peddlers he had to compete with? No! Whatever Sam's fate, he would not stoop to that. "But this way, I may at least get news of him," David told himself.

That day the rumor that Ross and Thompson had had a clash with Factor Colen flew thick and fast inside the post. "No doubt he thinks he'll have us eating out of his hand before the end of winter," Malcolm Ross exploded that evening, when Jack and Alf questioned him about the interview. "But maybe he's in for a surprise. With timid ones like Colen directing things, no wonder the bold ones like the two Mackenzies, Simon Fraser and the rest have quit the company and gone over to the Nor'westers. And they won't be the last," Ross added darkly.

"Not toying with the idea of desertion, are you, Malcolm?" Jack Jennings drawled.

"That's my business," David heard his new partner retort hotly.

Jack's somewhat jeering chuckle made Ross turn on him. "And suppose I was? Would I open my mouth about it before a brace of milk-and-water clerks like you?" The raw-boned young Scot was in a fiery mood this evening.

"Easy, now," Alf protested. "Why take it out on us?"

Malcolm Ross, his burst of anger over, looked a bit shamefaced. "Sorry. But when a man's trapped, he wants to fight back at somebody. And after all this stir about the Athabasca! If you think I'm riled, how do you suppose Thompson feels?"

Alf nodded. "Set you back on your haunches pretty hard, eh Dave?"

David did not answer. At that particular moment, his thoughts had turned again to Sam. Indians had long memories. Even if Sam had managed to get south, one of them would know. Besides, Malcolm had said too much already. After what the craving for promotion had done to a kindly man like Mr. Colen, a fellow never knew. Alf and Jack were dependent on his favors. Idle talk had a way of getting twisted.

"Least said, soonest mended, eh?" Jack asked him. "Is that the way of it?"

"More or less."

David knew that Philip Turnor could have taught him in one day more than he could master in a month by himself. But what was done, was done. There was no use in crying over spilled milk. He had the books of calculations and the precious sextant Mr. Turnor had given him, and all the Factor Colens this side of the North Pole could not prevent him from going on with his studies. Already his mind was made up. Dreary as the Muskrat Country was, he would have six solid months there, at the very least, to train himself for the career which, some way, some day, was going to be his.

Five days later, no sooner had the two large canoes rounded the point and swung into the broad channel of the Nelson River than David Thompson, sitting amidships, opened his notebook and got out his pocket compass, to begin his first serious attempt at mapping.

"Now what's the game?" Bill Cook, the green assistant, asked.

As the *voyageurs* and Indians bent to their paddles, David explained. "Look you, Bill. I want you to check our rate of travel by objects on the shore, while I jot down compass bearings."

Bill Cook who, like the older apprentices, had picked up rumors concerning the factor's jealousy of Mr. Turnor, and knew his prejudice against mapping, hesitated. "Haven't you got yourself into hot water enough?" he asked with an uneasy glance at the canoemen. "These fellows are bound to talk, and sooner or later this will get to the factor's ears."

David steadied his compass on the thwart. "And to his eyes as well, for if I'm satisfied that this map I'm going to make is true, Mr. Colen shall have a copy."

Bill shook his head. He was a curly-headed, apple-cheeked English boy, anxious to please. But, unfortunately, his months under Alf and Jack Jennings had done little to encourage his initiative. "He'd never send it to London, not from all I hear."

"Perhaps not. But he'll get his copy anyway."

Bill waggled his head. "My word, Dave, you're a queer one! Why a map, when our Indians know this country from end to end?" He waited. "However, if you want me to—"

"I do," David told him with finality.

After leaving York Factory on September 5th, 1792, and heading west from Hudson's Bay, David Thompson persisted in his surveys. By the end of the month the two canoes were well above Split Lake, where Malcolm and his party turned aside to ascend the Grass River, leaving David, Bill and their men to continue up the main stream to Sipiwisk Lake. Here, after several days spent in scouting for a site, David built his first trading post. It was sheltered between two rocky points of a small bay, protected by a good stand of forest at the rear, and faced the east and south, to take full advantage of the short hours of sunlight.

Every day counted now, for the freeze-up was close at hand. Long before sun-up, all hands turned out to labor in the crisp air. Axe blows rang sharply through the hushed woods. By mid-morning, in contrast to the nights, the men found themselves uncomfortably warm. Stripped down to their woolen vests, they raised their log walls, tier by tier. David and three of his French Canadians took the posts of most responsibility, notching and saddling the corners, while the rest dragged the logs and hoisted them into place. Then came the roof of overlapping puncheon, and the claw and boulder fireplace. There was firewood to cut and haul, and the canoe to be cached under a brush shelter for the winter.

With so many pressing tasks, there was little time for hunting and fishing to augment the supply of dry food they had brought with them from York. But when the work eased up somewhat, parties were sent out. Moosemeat, venison and great quantities of whitefish and trout were needed. But due to Factor Colen's bungling, they had been sent into an area almost destitute of game or fish. After the ice had set and the first snows transformed the forests, grumbling was heard. No Indians came their way, and had it not been for the rabbit snares, there would have been lean times indeed.

But with his objective clearly in mind, David at least had little time to dwell upon the ever-present hardships. On clear nights, while the others lounged around the narrow, high-throated fireplace, he would wrap himself against the cold, and with Black Boy for company set up his instruments in the snow of one of the rocky points.

151

From across the shadowy lake would come the high-pitched yapping of the foxes. And at intervals when a timber wolf sent its long-drawn-out hunger call quavering through the spruce forest, Black Boy's fur would rise and his lips bare in a soundless snarl. Even when the cold was so severe that the rumble of cracking ice came from all the lakes around, and the northern lights shifted and rolled in their eerie sky dance, the faithful Newfoundland stood guard beside his master.

Sometimes when David's fingers became so numbed that he must stop work and beat his hands together, he would become aware of the sound of singing coming from the cabin in the dark hollow below. One of the *voyageurs* had fashioned himself a crude fiddle and to the accompaniment of its sprightly squeak, David could hear the lusty voices chorusing such old-time favorites as *"En Roulant Ma Boule," "Gaie la Rose"* and the beautiful yet haunting *"À la Claire Fontaine."* Against the darkened wall of evergreens, sparks would fly upward as another log was thrown upon the fire. Then silence would come and he knew his men slept.

Once, long past midnight, when David packed his instruments and raced Black Boy down to the cabin, he found Bill Cook waiting up for him beside the fire.

"They're growing more puzzled than ever over what you're up to," Bill confided with a glance toward the sleeping *voyageurs* at the far end of the room. "They can't imagine what any man in his right senses would be doing out there, night after night, half-perished with cold and staring through a telescope."

"Why didn't you tell them, Bill?" David asked lightly, spreading his hands and hunching closer to the cheery blaze. "Surely you know by now I'm not intent on hiding my surveying from the factor."

"I did try to explain. But they simply cannot fathom it. They've got their own suspicions. Fact is, they half believe you're up to some kind of sorcery—reading the future in the heavens."

"Then I'll jolly soon put them right," David declared.

"But it does put them in awe of you," Bill suggested. "They are coming to think you a mighty man indeed." He paused. "It might give you a stronger hold on them, if trouble comes later on."

David stirred the fire impatiently. "I don't think much of a person who would trade on the superstitions of other men."

Bill gave David a long look. "Guess what the Indians are calling you? They call you 'Koo-Koo-Sint.' "

It took David a second or two to translate. "The-Man-Who-Looks-at-the-Stars, eh? Well, in a way that's true enough."

"But what do you think Mr. Colen will do when he hears it?" Bill cautioned. "He'll put two and two together. And since it's already plain our venture here will be a failure, it will allow him to fasten the blame for lack of furs on you. He'll excuse his error in sending us into the Muskrat Country by reporting to London that you were so busy with your own affairs you did not attend to the company's business."

"I had not thought of it in that light," Dave admitted soberly.

From the few Indians who were now coming to trade, David learned two important facts, both of which were vastly encouraging. One was that a young white man with a scar on his face had wintered a day or two's travel to the south with a band of the Muskrat people during David's first season at York, and in the spring had gone south with a party of independent traders. Only last fall he had been seen at Grand Portage, the Nor'westers' headquarters at the mouth of the Pigeon River. The second was that, besides the route to Lake Athabasca which Mr. Turnor had located, there was one north from the Churchill River to Reindeer Lake, and thence by way of the Black River to the east of Lake Athabasca. Long before the spring break-up, David completed his plans to explore this new route.

"I'd wait for orders if I were you," Bill Cook urged. "It's inviting trouble to go exploring on your own initiative."

David quite agreed. "Just the same, I'm going to make the trip. Knowing Mr. Colen's prejudices, how far do you think I'd get if I asked for help? And, besides, there isn't time to send a courier asking his permission."

As soon as the lakes and rivers were open, David sent his party, under Bill Cook, to York Factory. Weeks before this he had arranged to have several friendly Indians—the same ones who had brought him news of Sam—meet him at the Churchill River and guide him northward. When he had seen Bill's party started, David Thompson and one Indian canoeman set out for the distant rendezvous.

The far northern days were lengthening swiftly and though patches of snow lingered in the shade of the spruce thickets, the river banks were green with sprouting grasses, the bays and backwaters stippled with the tips of growing reeds. After the winter's confinement at Sipiwisk, the urge for new scenes and new experiences was strong upon David. No doubt Bill was right in saying Mr. Colen would be displeased, but in order to find out more about this new route this was a chance he was willing to take.

Day after day, the long reaches of water sparkling in the spring breezes gave a lift to his heart, inviting him to discover what lay beyond the next bend and over the next portage. At night, healthily tired, he lay on his bed of balsam boughs, lulled by the soft sound of flowing water or the distant, deep-throated marching song of the river's falls or rapids. It was good to be out on your own like this, talking your companion's native language, thinking his thoughts, living his carefree life, with the responsibilities of the trading post command laid aside for the time being.

But when they reached the Churchill River, David found that his Indian guides had failed him. He wasted days camping at the meeting place, waiting in vain for them to appear. Had he been able to bring back conclusive information concerning the new route, he might have justified his independent move. But now there was nothing for it but to descend through Burntwood Lake to the Nelson River and take the reprimand awaiting him.

But to David's profound astonishment, there was no reprimand. "You are to be commended, Thompson," Factor Colen told him.

David was speechless. He could not believe his ears.

"Yes, indeed," the factor assured him, continuing to examine the map the young explorer had put into his hands. "London will be greatly pleased with this. And, er—about taking it on yourself to search out a new route to the Athabasca, you need have no fear on that score. True, you exceeded your authority, but I shall protect you to the full." The factor's smile was bland, cordial.

More puzzled than ever, as soon as he had been dismissed, David hurried to Jack Jennings and Alf Robinson to ask what explanation they had for this astounding change of front.

"Simple enough," Alf snorted. "He's using you to pull his chestnuts out of the fire."

"*His* chestnuts!"

"Exactly," Jack said. He winked knowingly. "You fellows

155

out in the wilderness are always one jump behind. It takes an office man to see what's going on behind the scenes." He explained how, the previous autumn, Colen had had him copy out a letter to the governors which said Thompson and Ross were being sent to the Athabasca.

David snapped his fingers excitedly. "That's what Ross thought at the time. But we all know it wasn't what the factor intended at all. It simply is not true!"

"Of course not. But it fooled our stodgy gentlemen in London. They don't know the vastness of this country. What's more to the point, they don't know Colen. He plays a deep game, and plays it well. Once again he has succeeded in pulling the wool over their eyes."

David shook his head in bewilderment. "All this is too deep for me."

"But don't you see?" Jack asked. "Word has come from London that they expect great things from your Athabasca venture—the very one you and Malcolm Ross planned and which Colen would not let you make. But since he went against London's orders, since, instead, he had you bury yourself in the Muskrat Country, this second letter put Colen in a bad light. I tell you he was worried. If the governors had found out what his game was, he might have been dismissed. And well he knows it."

Jack gave David a patronizing pat on the back. "Then along comes our innocent David and clears Colen by making this latest Athabasca try all on his own. No wonder he was purring like a cat over a saucer of cream. For the moment, you're his white-haired boy. You've saved his bacon, or chestnuts, or whatever you want to call it."

Alf, who relished intrigue, chuckled. "I fear you're not deep enough for company politics, Dave. Down-river you come, fearing the worst. But, instead, he greets you like a long-lost brother."

But for days this involved explanation was not clear to David Thompson. A senior factor, only one step lower in rank than Governor Hearne himself, haggling and deceiving and actually lying like some dishonest fishmonger! But presently, when the annual ship arrived from England, David learned how right Jack and Alf had been.

"I'm sending the chief inland full instructions," Factor Colen told David and Malcolm Ross after he had read the contents of the mail pouches. "You two will be going west with the brigade for the Saskatchewan. Then when you reach Cumberland House the chief inland will give you my detailed instructions." He rose and shook their hands. "Good luck and *bon voyage,*" he ended affably. "And again my thanks for your map, young Thompson."

After so friendly a send-off David allowed himself to believe that at last he and Malcolm were being assigned to really important work. But the canny young Scot was not so sure. "Sealed orders to the chief inland, eh? When everyone knows that Factor Tomison and Colen are at daggers drawn!"

David grinned. "For an open-handed Highlander, you've a suspicious nature when it comes to Colen."

"Laugh while you've the chance, Dave," Malcolm Ross growled. "Soon you may be laughing on t'other side of your face. If you ask me, Colen's up to his old tricks."

CHAPTER SEVENTEEN

After strenuous weeks, the flotilla of heavily loaded canoes put Lake Winnipeg behind them and in due course reached Cumberland House. This was a well-established post, the first one of the company inland, built by Samuel Hearne almost two decades ago, in 1774. After his year in the bleak Muskrat Country, David was delighted to be back once more in this rich land of wooded bluffs and rolling grassland. But hardly had he and Malcolm arrived before the latter's suspicions of Colen were confirmed.

Colen's orders made no mention of the Athabasca. Instead, Malcolm was posted to trading duty in the area, while David was ordered to proceed to Buckingham House, upriver.

"This is more than I can stomach," Malcolm blazed when they were outside, after having had the chief inland read Colen's instructions for them. "I'd give a year's pay to have the governors learn of this."

"You mean you'd kick over the traces, Malcolm? You mean you'd write them?"

"Aye. But trust Colen to wait until he had us a thousand miles inland before he showed his hand. Not only that, but by now the annual ship will be on her way home. The way it is now, 'twill be twelve months before there's a mail—and twelve months more before an answer can be brought. Which means that Colen's word is law out here for two whole years."

The disappointed pair sat down on the sunny cut-bank beside the river. "If only some of the governors had first-hand knowledge of this country," David said.

Malcolm picked up a chip and tossed it disgustedly into the swirling water. "That's a big 'if,' Davvie. Yon gentlemen of quality like comfort too well to leave the Old Land. But it's high time we out here—all of us—see to it they learn of what is going on, for if Colen keeps on the way he has been going, it will not be long before the company's trade will be ruined. No, lad, the company's future is our future, too. If only for our own sakes, we all must find some way to have Colen put in his place."

David was about to make some comment when Black Boy, who had retrieved the chip Malcolm had thrown, scrambled up the bank, dropped his trophy at his master's feet and shook himself so vigorously that he drenched the pair of them. But instead of protesting, Malcolm gave the old dog a friendly slap on the back. "The more I see of some men, the more I like a good dog like you, Boy," he declared. He rubbed his chin. "I'm sick at heart at all this everlasting scheming, Davvie."

159

"I wish my time was served, but I'm still only an apprentice. I should be sending money home. Yet here I am, tied hand and foot." David hesitated. "But you're a full-fledged junior officer, Malcolm. If you protested, the governors would at least hear your case."

"My guess is your word will carry more weight than mine. A good, reliable map talks a thousand times stronger than a letter. We musn't go off at half cock, that I know. But what do you say we pledge ourselves to stand together in all this? And to act together when our chance comes?"

"You can count on me," David said. They sealed their pledge of protest with a handshake. A few days later they had to go their separate ways. But they both knew they were in the right, even though what they had made amounted to a pact of rebellion.

David Thompson did good work that winter. From Buckingham House, he rode still farther west into the Beaver Hills near the site of what, far in the future, would be the city of Edmonton, Canadian gateway to the North. And here, as during his expedition into the Blackfoot country, the pull was westward. This wide pass through the Rockies might well be the main door to the fabulous Pacific. Here in the wide valleys, on peaks and timbered slopes, wild life abounded. The jewel-like lakes and cold mountain streams held trout of astounding size and vigor. Generations hence all this would be known as Jasper National Park, and the wonderment the young explorer felt would be shared by vacationers from the Old World and the New.

Retracing his trail eastward, David surveyed the Saskatchewan down to the forks, and from there accurately resurveyed the rest of that great river. Each survey increased his proficiency, and the sense of being thwarted left him for a time.

After the breakup he was given authority by the chief inland to explore a new route through Goose, Reed and Burntwood Lakes to the Nelson River, and in so doing opened up a better trail to York Factory.

All this was exacting but immensely satisfying work for David. His uncanny gift of correctly measuring rates of travel, his ability to retain clear mental pictures of the country, his instinct for direction, all these helped him. And with them went a scientific zeal for accuracy and an attention to detail which were remarkable. Then, too, he had an active curiosity which led him to explore creek mouths, bays and alternate routes and so enabled him to gain an intimate knowledge of the country as a whole.

But vital to his achievements as all these were, it was his ever-growing loyalty to the country, along with his deep sense that this wild land was his and that, unlike most of the Englishmen and Scots with whom he served, he belonged to it and was its adopted son, which unified and directed all his efforts. The Canada he knew might be all its critics said of it—a wild, barbaric land—but it had been bringing him a sense of home increasingly since that stormy night in Manchester House.

Also, as his diary began to reveal, he was beginning to foresee the shape of things to come. Furs and profits were the main concern of his associates, while he was noting the richness of the soil, the wealth of grazing land and boundless forest. Young as he was, he sometimes pictured the day, generations hence, when the poor and landless of the Old World would come in and possess it. Not forever would the great company be able to hold it and its native population for themselves in a state of feudalism. Maps, and ever more maps, were needed, and come what might, he would go on making them.

When David arrived at York Factory he was delighted to find the annual ship already at its moorings. This headquarters post, founded as early as 1682, and which had changed hands seven times during the French wars, had long been the metropolis for the isolated traders inland. If they were lucky, they were able to enjoy its comforts and excitement once a year, to talk with fellow countrymen fresh from England, to discuss the news and gossip of the day.

This year David Thompson found York Factory seething with excited rumor. From what Jack Jennings told him, resentment against Factor Colen's intrigue and scheming for his personal advantage was coming to a head. Then on the day that Malcolm Ross, travel-stained but full of fight, reached York, Alf Robinson secretly showed him and David a letter to the factor, freshly arrived from the governors in London.

"Here, Davvie," Ross urged. "You read it."

David's crisp Welsh voice began:

"We are perfectly satisfied with the conduct of Messrs David Thompson, Ross and others . . . But obstacles are again, we perceive, thrown in the way of the Athabasca Expedition . . . We trust all difficulties which occur and impede the Company's success will be removed."

This last was obviously a warning.

"At last!" Ross declared. "They've seen through his trickery at last!" He looked at David. "No need now to inform the governors about all Colen's bungling inland."

"That's for you chaps to decide," Alf commented nervously. "But either way, you'd better make up your minds tonight, for the ship sails at dawn tomorrow."

Malcolm reflected. "But surely this letter sets matters

162

straight. Let's have a second look at it. ' . . . *all difficulties which occur and impede the company's success will be removed.*' If that isn't putting it straight to Colen, I don't know what is. Now he'll no longer dare thwart the Athabasca venture."

If only Malcolm and David could have known how completely they were being hoodwinked! For at that very moment, where the lighted window of the factor's quarters showed in contrast to the shadow of the stockade, Colen was busy penning a letter, full of quibbling and mock humility, to the governors in London. In it, as the records later revealed, he was throwing all the blame for the Athabasca failure on the veteran Tomison, far away on the Saskatchewan. It was Tomison's lack of co-operation, nay, his scheming hostility, which had prevented Thompson and Ross from carrying out the sealed orders he himself had sent to the chief inland. What Colen did not include in his report was the contents of those orders. And, to round out his lie, he stated that there had also been insubordination among the canoemen. He was sure, he finished, that the governors would approve of the steps he was now taking to carry out their wishes.

The trick worked. Next morning, after the ship had weighed anchor and the last link with England had been cut for another long year, Ross and Thompson received their orders. With William Cook and two other juniors, Tate and Sinclair, they were again sentenced to another winter in the Muskrat Country, which Colen, still ignoring the company's interests farther west, was jealously guarding as his own preserve.

Malcolm's reaction to this crowning deception was a curious one. Whether his winter under the chief inland had somewhat cooled his ardor for Western exploration, or whether he had become so disgusted with the London governors' gullibility, David could only guess. But, whatever his reason, the Scot seemed to have decided on tactics other than those he had discussed with David at Cumberland House the previous fall.

"If it's trickery he wants," Malcolm said grimly, "he'll see that two can play at that game. And, anyway, since the governors are fools enough to be taken in by him, why should we do their fighting for them?"

David asked what he intended to do.

"Keep my mouth shut and my eyes open—and look after myself," Ross answered bitterly. "And if you've a mind for your own interests, Davvie, you'll do the same. Why should we break our necks to see the Athabasca?"

"I still intend to see it, though," David said.

"So? Well, your beard will be gray if you wait till Colen sends you."

That winter, one of the coldest in the history of the Bay, David spent at Reed Lake in the Muskrat Country. Game and fish were fairly plentiful in that region, but the cold was so intense and the snow so deep that even the local Indians were prevented from working their traplines to the usual extent. As a result, the trade was poor, and David and his assistant had much free time on their hands.

David, for his part, put this to good use by daily application to his navigation studies. The problems in the textbooks Philip Turnor had given him were stiff ones. But already he had gained enough practical experience to go about solving them. In addition, he drafted maps from his field notes of recent surveys, so that when spring came he had the satisfaction of knowing his winter had not been wasted.

The poor trade that winter was its own justification for abandoning the Reed Lake post and when, in July, David paddled down-river, he realized that the few bales of furs in the canoe would certainly do nothing to overcome the factor's all-too-apparent hostility to Malcolm and himself. Though he did not know it then, it was to be his last visit to the great York Factory.

On his arrival there, he was astounded by the news that Factor Colen had just taken ship for England.

"Full of self-importance, as usual," the bluff old surgeon snorted. "No doubt he got wind of the representations some of us are making to the governors and decided that by going there himself he could put us out of face." He waggled his head at others of the staff. "But he's not done with us yet, is he, gentlemen?"

This was David's first inkling of a further move on the part of the officers. But as he sat among them on the long bench outside the guardroom door, he soon learned that they had determined to draw up a round robin, signed by all of them, setting forth the details of Colen's years of misrule.

"We'll have it in England hard on Colen's heels, too," one of them insisted. "The *Rupert* has not yet cleared out of Churchill. And even if it has, there's the Moose River route. We can get our statement out by Montreal before the river freezes."

David said nothing. Armed with his valuable maps, his position was a strong one. There were men in America as well as England who would understand their importance and would pay well for them.

But that was not David Thompson's way. For one thing, he was still articled to the company and desertion now would be a breach of faith. And for another, only by all hands at York standing shoulder to shoulder could they bring matters to a head.

"At all costs we must avoid the impression getting abroad in London that we here are a parcel of malcontents," the surgeon was saying. "Whoever takes the lead in this must be one whose work here has inspired some confidence among the governors."

"Exactly," the head clerk agreed. "And that's why I maintain Thompson here must be the one. I've seen the letters back and forth. The governors appreciate his surveys. And Colen has played into our hands by the praise he has heaped on Thompson from time to time in his London dispatches. Of course," the head clerk added, "in doing this he managed to give the impression that David Thompson was his protégé and a thoroughgoing Colen man."

"But I'm not!" David protested. "You ask Malcolm Ross. Ask him to tell you of the words which passed between us and the factor."

"Of course you're not," the surgeon agreed. "That's not the way the head clerk means it. What he's saying is that someone must take the lead in drawing up our statement, and that if you take a prominent part in this, it will knock the wind out of Colen's sails more than if the letter were penned by any other of us.

"Will you do it?" the surgeon asked suddenly, clapping David on the shoulder. "Good lad. Say you will."

"I've evidence aplenty of my own to prove his misrule," David answered. "But I'm still an apprentice, don't forget. That makes a difference. I'd like time to think this over."

Later in the evening, Alf Robinson sought David out. "This round robin is our only possible move, I grant. But why should you be the one who sticks his head into the noose? Let some of the older ones do that, for if the protest is in your handwriting, Colen will nail you sure."

"Some of the evidence against him must come from me. He'll guess that the moment he sets eyes on it. And, anyway, I know I'm in the right. I intend to put my name to every charge I make."

166

Alf gave a low whistle. "Laid your ears back properly, haven't you, Davvie?"

"I have," David agreed. That evening he began to draft the letter. Citing time and place and circumstances, every officer at York gave evidence against their factor. Nor was David Thompson's share in the round robin by any means the least damning. Then, some time later, he wrote a personal letter to Factor Colen.

"Many of us," that historic letter concluded, "acknowledge with readiness that you have some good qualities, and I once had the greatest respect for you. I have none now but—it is not my wish to say those things you do not wish to hear. How is it, sir, that everyone who has once wished you well should turn to be indifferent to you now, and even some to hate you, although they have been constant in their other friendships? There must be a defect somewhere. The fact is that from your peculiar manner of conduct you are also one of those unfortunate men who will have many an acquaintance, but never a real friend."

But, in part, David was wrong. He had been thinking of veterans like Tomison, Longmore and Mitchell Oman, and, most of all, of his benefactor Philip Turnor, when he wrote that letter. But as he was to discover some months later, Factor Colen did have some friends left—and those among the powerful in the councils of the company in London—who would follow him to take his revenge on the writer of the York round robin.

CHAPTER EIGHTEEN

THE STAFF'S RESENTMENT over the intrigues of their absent factor made life at York Factory so unsettling that David Thompson and Malcolm Ross were both relieved when it was time for them to leave. With good parchment and India ink available, David made the final copy of his last year's map. When this was sealed, ready for dispatch, he added the final pages to his letter to his mother. Fortunately, according to her letter, conditions were much improved. He was not to worry about them, she said. Her letter was so hopeful he decided to say nothing about his own troubles. Had Jem Little not left the company's service to accept a berth aboard a merchantman, David would have liked to have him deliver the box of Indian curios he had brought from the Saskatchewan. As it was, he selected small presents of beaded leather and entrusted them to the mails.

This done, he set to work selecting his next winter's trade goods and supplies and prepared to start again for the dreary Muskrat Country, for before his abrupt departure for London, Factor Colen had left written instructions for him to do so.

"Another winter at Reed Lake, eh?" Jack Jennings asked sympathetically.

"Reed Lake, nothing!" David told him. "Luckily for Malcolm and me, the orders are rather general ones. No particular areas are mentioned. So this time I'm going farther north. I'll build my post on Duck portage, on the trail between Burntwood Lake and the upper Churchill."

"Is that much better than where you were last winter?" Jack wanted to know.

"It's better in this way—I'll be that much nearer the start of the new Athabasca route which the directors still want explored."

"You still believe they do?"

"You know yourself, Jack, they've said so all along. And all Colen's talk will never make them change their minds. It has become a matter of company policy. Mr. Colen's been delaying it, that's all. I've been talking to Alf about it and he thinks that my marching orders will arrive with next year's ship. So when they do, will you see that I get them quickly, by courier? The directors have also promised me a new *Nautical Almanac*. My old one's so out-dated it's not much help with the surveying."

David and his small party set out a few days after Malcolm

had started for Fairford House, a small post near the mouth of Reindeer River. As on previous journeys, Black Boy went along. When wind and current favored the paddlers, he rode; when the going was hard, he was put ashore and followed them along the bank. This he preferred to the inactivity of sitting in his master's canoe. There were rabbits to run, grouse to flush, and now and then a moose or black bear, drowsing in the heat of the day in some shady spot, to bring to its feet with outraged snorts.

Traveling without unnecessary haste, living as much as possible on the game and fish the country provided, the party reached Duck portage in ample time to erect a small post and make good provision for the winter. Trading proved moderately good for an area so much trapped, so that David was kept busy most of the time with routine tasks. But when spring came with its unsettling urge, he found himself eager for the arrival of the annual mail.

Once again the poplars and willows were in leaf; once more David Thompson saw the green saucers of water lily leaves resting on pool and reedy backwater; once again those pests of the North, which in his diary he called "musketoes," were buzzing. His years in the country had given him a certain immunity to them but, even so, on close evenings smudges must be lighted at the door of the post building. The winter's take of furs was baled, the two canoes were overhauled and freshly seamed with pitch, extra paddles shaped, and the post put in readiness for the men to leave. And then one noon the packet Indian or post messenger came.

David's fingers trembled a little as he undid the mail pouch. There were his orders, sure enough. They contained Factor Colen's formal permission to explore the new Athabasca route.

Still reading, David reached out and rumpled Black Boy's silky ears. "We're really going this time, old fellow," he confided. And then he stiffened, for closer examination of the dispatch revealed that Mr. Colen was still up to his old tricks.

"Look here," David exploded to his assistant. "He has given me permission to make the trip, all right. But there is no provision whatever for equipment or canoemen—no help of any kind. And on top of that he has held back my *Almanac!*"

The factor's duplicity had all but wrecked the expedition before it began. But the London gentlemen would not guess that. Ignorant of Northern conditions, they would not realize that permission alone meant nothing; that without extra men or equipment, or even a canoe, the Athabasca exploration was doomed.

"Here's what we'll do," David decided. He spoke quietly, grimly. "We'll turn in our furs to Malcolm at Fairford House. Malcolm's heart is in this venture, too, and I dare say he'll find ways of giving me some help."

With this faith in his old comrade, David led his party westward. But at Fairford House further obstacles confronted him.

"I'm sorry, Davvie," Ross told him. "Colen has been making things as difficult as he can for me. We're short-handed as it is and I dare not spare you one man or a canoe."

"But read it for yourself! The directors expect me to make this trip!"

"Aye, I know they do. But see the trick the fox Colen is playing on you? By this order he has squared himself with the governors. If there's failure, the fault is entirely yours, or so it will seem to them."

"That's plain enough."

"Either way, he has you where he wants you, Davvie. If you don't go—and with no outfit, how can you?—you'll be blamed; and if you do, like as not you'll never be heard of again. Nor would I put it past Colen to be taking this way of getting rid of one who took a leading part in that round robin affair. To him that was out-and-out revolt, you know."

"I don't think so."

"Nor I," Malcolm agreed. "But, even so, I'm afraid he's got you."

"Not if I succeed, he hasn't."

"That's a big 'if.' From the head of Reindeer Lake to the Athabasca is bad country, so the Indians have been telling me this winter. Even they avoid it like the plague."

David became lost in thought. This strange urge which, all through history, had lured men beyond the boundaries of the known, was not a delusion, leading men to their own destruction. It was not curiosity nor a shallow restlessness. True, men like Philip Turnor had fared badly at its hands. True, it was the shrewd ones, the traders, schemers like Joseph Colen, who stood in highest favor with the company. But there were others who in all fields of human endeavor must be pathfinders, whatever the cost. It was in their blood.

"It's a poor chance, Malcolm, I know," David admitted. "But even a poor chance may not come my way again."

"You mean you're going?"

"If you can find me two good men among the local Indians."

Malcolm hesitated. "As your friend, I should be doing all I can to block this dangerous move—not helping you to risk your neck. But I know the stuff you're made of, and I do believe you'll manage to come through. Let's walk over to the Chepawyan encampment."

Of this visit and what led up to it, David Thompson wrote in his diary as follows:

"Finding that I could have no white men to accompany me somewhat dampened my ardour, but my curiosity to see unknown countries prevailed and, a few Chepawyans happening to be there, and had traded in their furs, I engaged two

172

young men of them to accompany me. Both of them had hunted for two winters over the country we were to explore, but had never been on the rivers and lakes in the summer. Their only practice in canoes had been on a calm day to watch for the Deer taking refuge from the flies, and for Otters and Fowls, which gave them no experience of the currents and rapids of the rivers.

"Yet such as they were, I was obliged to take them. They were both unmarried young men. One of them, named Kozdaw, was of a powerful, active make; gay, thoughtless, and ready for every kind of service; would climb the trees and brave the Eagles in their nests; yet under all this wildness was a kind and faithful heart. The other, from his hard name which I could not pronounce, I named Paddy. He was of a slender form, thoughtful, of a mild disposition.

"As nothing whatever was ready for us, we had to go into the Forests for all the materials to make a canoe; of seventeen feet in length by thirty inches on the middle bar.

"Early on the tenth day of June 1795 we were ready. Our outfit consisted of one fowling gun; forty balls, five pounds of shot, three flints and five pounds of powder, one net of thirty fathoms; one small axe, a small Tent of gray cotton; with a few trifles to trade provisions, as beads, brass rings and awls, of which we had little hope; our chief dependence, next to good Providence, was on our Net and Gun."

With so small a craft, and after repeated warnings from the Indians about the lack of food throughout the country into which they were venturing, Dave reluctantly decided to leave Black Boy in Malcolm's care. The big Newfoundland, now past his prime, could not be expected to hunt his food in such a country.

During those last days of preparation, Black Boy acted as if he understood. Everywhere Dave went, he was at his heels, his soft eyes following his master's every move, his ears lifting to catch the sound of every word he spoke. But when the time of parting came, he made no effort to climb into the canoe.

David felt a lump in his throat as his eyes met those of his faithful friend. "You look after Malcolm," he finally managed to say. "I know he'll look after you." Then with a hurried pat, he stepped into the canoe. A hundred yards from the landing, when he ventured to glance back, he saw Black Boy, tail and ears drooping, sadly following Malcolm up the path.

David and his two young Indians paddled up the Reindeer River sixty miles to Reindeer Lake. "The banks are of sloping high rock," he wrote. "The woods of small Birch, Aspin and Pines, growing on rocks with little soil . . . The Natives are frequently very careless in putting out the fires they make, and a high wind kindles it among the pines . . . which makes the country very unsightly and destroys many animals and birds."

After they had left Reindeer Lake and coasted the west side of Manito Lake for eighty miles, the party made camp on the evening of June twenty-third at the head of Black River. Around their meager fire that night, David questioned Kozdaw and Paddy about the great lake spreading away into the unknown north.

"By their information this lake is of very great extent," he recorded. "The eighty miles we coasted they count as nothing. They say that none has seen its northern part . . . the deep, long rolling waves in a gale of wind . . . showed it a very deep lake and that the roll of waves come from a great distance . . . It is a pity the Hudson's Bay Company do not have these countries explored; by their charter they hold these extensive countries to the exclusion of all other persons."

Day after day, paddling and portaging ever deeper into the unknown, David felt more vividly than ever before the bond of brotherhood between himself and the two who shared his adventure with him.

174

He wrote:

"By civilized man ... especially those ... who have a mortal antipathy to the North American Indian or, as he is now called, the Red Man, it is confidently held that the Red Man must soon cease to exist and give place to the White Man. This is true of all the lands formerly possessed by the Red Man, that the White Man has thought it worth his while to seize by fraud or force.

"But the Stony region is an immense tract of country, on which the White Man cannot live except by hunting, which he will not submit to. Here is an immense tract of country which the Supreme Being, the Lord of the whole Earth, has given to the Deer and other animals; and to the Red Man forever. Here, as his fathers of many centuries past have done, he may roam, free as the wind. But this wandering life and the poverty of the country prevents the labours of the Missionary to teach them the sacred truths of Christianity."

Days later, when they had crossed Hatchet Lake, which David described as "a wretched country of solitude, broken only by the large Gull and the Loons," they reached the thundering falls on Black River. And it was here that David saw Kozdaw and Paddy yield to the dark superstition into whose clutches their ignorance and what he termed "lack of true religion" had led them.

Here they found this great river compressed between walls of rock only twelve yards apart.

"At the end of this channel a bold, perpendicular point of limestone projects at right angles to the course of the river, against which the rapid current rushes and appears driven back with such force that the whole river seems as if turned up from its bottom.

"It boils, foams and every drop is white. Part of the water is driven down a precipice of twenty feet descent; the greater part rushes through a point of rock and disappears for two hundred yards, then issues out in boiling whirlpools. The dashing of the water against the rocks, the deep roar of the torrent, the hollow sound of the fall, with the surrounding high, frowning hills, form a scenery grand and awful, and it is well named Manito (supernatural) fall. . . ."

Standing there, drenched with mist and deafened by the sound, David saw Paddy throw in his brass ring and Kozdaw some other small treasure as an offering to the dark and vengeful spirit of the rapids. But David, arms folded, his long hair beaded with spray, stared down into the dizzy caldron and by his manner made it plain to his companions that he would have no part in their superstitious rites.

"From the Manito to the Athabasca Lake, by the course of the Black river and its Lakes, is 162 miles of varied country, but the farther west the better. And the bold, high, sloping wooded hills of the Athabasca Lake had something soft and pleasing. This journey was attended by much danger, toil and suffering . . . This great lake had been surveyed by Mr. Philip Turnor in 1791. He had lopped and marked a pine tree at which we passed the night. This was the second of July.

"On our return, about half way up the Black River, we came to one of the falls, with a strong rapid above and below it. We had a carrying place of 200 yards. We then attempted the strong current above the fall. They were to track the canoe up on a line, walking on shore, while I steered it.

"But when they had proceeded about eighty yards they came to a Birch Tree, growing at the edge of the water, and there stood and disputed between themselves on which side of the tree the line should pass. I called on them to go on. They could not hear me for the noise of the fall. I then waved my hand for them to proceed. Meanwhile the current was drifting me out, and having only one hand to guide the canoe, the Indians standing still, the canoe took a sheer across the current. To prevent the canoe upsetting, I waved my hand for them to let go the line and leave me to my fate, which they obeyed.

"I sprang to the bow of the canoe and cut the line . . . By this time I was at the head of the fall. All I could do was to place the canoe to go down bow foremost. In an instant the canoe was precipitated down the fall (twelve feet) and buried under the waves. I was struck out of the canoe, and when I rose among the waves, the canoe came on me and buried me beneath it.

"To raise myself I struck my feet against the rough bottom and came up close to the canoe which I grasped, and being now in shoal water, guided it to shore. My two companions ran to my assistance. Nothing remained in the canoe but an axe, a small tent of gray cotton and my gun. . . . I lay down on the rocks, wounded, bruised and exhausted from my exertions. . . . On rising from my rocky bed, I perceived much blood at my left foot. On looking at it, I found the flesh of my foot, from the heel to near the toe, torn away. . . .

"It was now our destitute condition stared us in the face. A long journey through barren country, without provisions or the means of obtaining any, almost naked, and suffering from the weather. All before us was very dark, but I had hopes that the Supreme Being, through our Great Redeemer, to whom I made my short prayers morning and evening, would find some way to preserve us."

CHAPTER NINETEEN

THE SIGHT OF BLOOD streaming from his mangled foot roused David Thompson to action. Stunned and half-drowned though he was, he realized he must plan swiftly if they were not to leave their bones in this Northern wilderness.

"Paddy! Kozdaw! Downstream quickly. Save what you can from the rapids," he shouted above the booming of the falls.

With the quick-thinking Kozdaw in the lead, the pair charged down the shallows. David fell to his knees again, dragged the sodden tent to him and tore bandages to stop the flow of blood.

The half-hour before the two Chepawyan youths returned seemed like an eternity. Topping all their other losses was the thought that almost all their clothes were gone, for in lining the canoe up the white water, they had been wading practically naked.

At last, beyond the shoulder of spray-drenched rock, David could see Kozdaw returning. He was empty-handed.

"You could find nothing?" David gasped.

"I ran ahead to help you," Kozdaw explained breathlessly. "Paddy has the three paddles and that box."

It was meager salvage indeed, considering their plight. Yet David Thompson's most prized possessions were in that cork-lined box—the Dollard sextant, his telescope, compass and survey notes, as well as the small Bible the headmaster of the Gray Coat School had given him years ago.

"What must we do now?" Kozdaw was asking. There had been times when Kozdaw's reckless high spirits had caused Dave to wish he were more like the quiet-mannered Paddy. But in a crisis like this, David was thankful he had so resourceful a comrade.

"Go quickly to the birch trees and get some touchwood," he urged. "We must make a fire."

As Kozdaw scrambled up the rocks, Paddy appeared with his load. David was so bruised and so dizzy from loss of blood that he could only point to the gun. When Paddy brought it, David took the flint from the lock. After striking it repeatedly against the blade of his knife, it threw a spark. By this time Kozdaw had returned with the touchwood and a ball of finely shredded birchbark. It was a tense moment until the wisp of smoke had been fanned into flame.

For two hours Paddy and Kozdaw melted pitch and patched the broken canoe. "Now cut the tent into three pieces," David instructed. "The nights will be colder from this time on, and without some sort of covering the mosquitoes will devour us."

179

His only clothes were his shirt and a thin linen vest and his comrades were even worse off. "Tie the cloth around you as best you can. When you're ready we will take ourselves out of this drenched hole."

As David swayed to his feet, Paddy protested. "You should rest first, Koo-koo-sint."

David shook his head. Without food of any kind, and no chance of finding any in this gloomy canyon, they must travel while strength remained.

Kozdaw motioned for Paddy to take the other end of their seventeen-foot birchbark canoe. David slung the strap of the cork box over his shoulder, picked up the three paddles, the gun and a pewter basin which Paddy had later rescued from an eddy, and hobbled in their wake.

By nightfall they had worked their way above the rapids. There they kindled a fire and, without a bite to eat, wrapped themselves each in his square of canvas and spent an uneasy night. David's own story continues:

"On the second day, in the afternoon, we came out on a small lake of the river, and in the grassy bay saw two large Gulls hovering. This led us to think they were taking care of their group. We went, found three young gulls which we put into the canoe. . . . These gulls gave us but little meat. They had not four ounces of meat on them. It appeared to sharpen hunger.

"The next day as we proceeded, I remembered an Eagle's Nest on the banks of a small lake before us. I enquired of my companions if the young eagles could fly. They said they are now large but cannot fly. I said do you not remember the Eagle's Nest before us? We shall be there by mid-day and get the young Eagles for our supper.

"Accordingly we came to the Lake and went to the Eagle's Nest. It was about sixteen feet from the ground, in the spreading branches of a birch tree. The old ones were absent. But Kozdaw was barely at the nest before they arrived and Paddy and myself, with shouts and pelting them with stones, with difficulty prevented the Eagles from attacking Kozdaw.

"He soon threw the two young Eagles down to us. They placed themselves on their backs, and with beak and claws fought for their lives. When apparently dead, Kozdaw incautiously laid hold of one of them, who immediately struck the claws of one foot deep into his arm above the wrist. So firm were the claws in his arm, I had to cut off the legs at the first joint. . . . Even then when we took out a claw, it closed again, and we had to put bits of wood under each claw until we got the whole out.

"We continued our journey to the evening, when as usual we put ashore and made a fire. On opening the young eagles, their insides appeared a mass of yellow fat, which we collected and with the meat divided into three portions. Paddy and myself eat only the inside fat, reserving the meat for next day. But we noticed Kozdaw roasting the meat and oiling himself with the fat."

That night David and Paddy were taken violently ill. "We continued our voyage day after day, subsisting on berries, mostly the crowberry, which grows on the ground and is not nutritious, to the sixteenth of July."

By this time, what with hunger, the cold nights and their persistent sickness, "Paddy and myself were," David wrote, "like skeletons."

"We were so weak we thought it useless to go any farther, but to die where we were. Kozdaw now burst into tears, upon which we told him that he was yet strong, as he had not suffered from the disease. He replied, if you both die, I am sure to be killed. For everyone will believe I have killed you both. The white men will revenge your death on me, and the Indians will do the same for him.

"I told him to get some thin white birch rind, and I would give him a writing, which I did. With charcoal I wrote a short account of our situation, which I gave him, upon which he said, I am now safe.

"However we got into the canoe and proceeded slowly. We were very weak when, thank God, in the afternoon we came to two tents of Chepawyans, who pitied our wretched condition. They gave us broth but would not allow us meat until next day. I procured some provisions, a flint and nine rounds of ammunition and a pair of shoes for each of us on credit, to be paid for when they came to trade, also an old kettle. We proceeded now with thanks to God and cheerful hearts. We killed two Swans and without any accident on the 21st July arrived at Fairford House from whence we had commenced our journey."

It would be a month at least before Malcolm and his party could be expected back from the annual canoe voyage down to York Factory. The post was closed, its paths and doorsteps overgrown with wild grass and Black Boy nowhere to be seen. But David had hardly unbarred the door and drawn the wooden pins which held the shutters before he heard the thud of soft feet behind him. Then, as he turned, the old dog reared, planted his forefeet on his master's shoulders and all but knocked him down in his ecstasy of delight.

"Easy, old fellow, easy!" David protested laughingly. He held the battle-scarred old head between his hands. "My, it's grand to see you! Either the rabbit hunting's good hereabouts, or someone is looking after you. You're certainly well-fed." And as Black Boy dropped to all fours, David stroked his glossy coat.

As the pair stood thus, grinning at each other, Paddy came down the rocks from the native camping place just beyond the point. "My grandfather and his wife stayed here. Your white friend paid them to look after your dog for you," he explained.

"He's in fine shape," David said. "Meat must be plentiful. Not like the country we have just traveled through."

"But it is not, Koo-koo-sint," Paddy answered. "Only for

182

the dried provisions Malcolm Ross left with them, the old people—and your dog—would have had a bad time of it."

This was an unexpected state of affairs, for here where the Reindeer River joined the upper reaches of the Churchill game had usually been plentiful. "From this time until the 26th August our time was spent in fishing and hunting," David Thompson recorded. "And with all our exertions we could barely maintain ourselves."

Something must be done. He and his two companions were still sorely undernourished due to their privations in the Athabasca terrain. After having found a new route into that great country, and being the first white man to see hundreds of miles of the North, David was eager to work up his field notes in time to have his new map submitted to the governors before the winter. In spite of Factor Colen's lack of support, he had added a great area to the known domain of his company. But his work would not be complete until he had it recorded and in permanent form. No wonder he begrudged every hour he had to spend in hunting.

And yet a man must eat, and so he laid aside his survey work and spent nearly all of his waking hours in the woods and along the shores of the two rivers. The spring had been a wet one and the hatch of partridge had been poor. From all indications, too, there was a dearth of rabbits. According to what his grandfather told Paddy, this was the fatal seventh year when the strange disease destroyed all but the hardy few. Now with no rabbits to fall back on, hunting must be done farther afield.

But for Black Boy at least, these were happy times. Day after day he went with his master. His knowledge of the ways of waterfowl was especially helpful. Not one bird which David's muzzle loader brought down was lost. No matter how swift the rapids or how dense the reed beds, Black Boy found them all.

At sunset one evening they were heading for the post when David decided to take a short-cut up the course of a small stream known locally as Sucker Creek. Because of the dry weather, its flow was reduced almost to a trickle and the stiff mud of the shrunken channel was ideal for tracking. Besides, a fox or wolf or even a bear might be attracted to the place in the hope of finding some of the soft, unpalatable fish for which the creek was named stranded between the dwindling pools.

Dusk came quickly between those ragged walls of willows and as they rounded a turn, a warning, tight-throated growl came from Black Boy. David peered ahead, but at first could see nothing. But the old Newfoundland's fur was up and David looked again. Partly hidden by some boulders thirty yards ahead, he saw a huge black bear. It stood with one great forepaw lifted, staring down into a trickle between the stones.

The current of night air sucking down the channel kept the bear from scenting them. David lowered himself to his knees, withdrew the bird shot from his muzzle loader, and put in two balls. Slowly he rose, moving slightly to the left until he had the bear's head and shoulders silhouetted against a patch of night sky. Twice he checked his aim, wishing belatedly he had had time to increase the powder charge, for the bear was the largest he had ever seen. Then he squeezed the trigger and the creek bed between the willows echoed to the shattering explosion.

David saw the bear lurch and go down and in the half-light concluded that his aim had been true and that he had got both balls in, just behind the upraised shoulder. He was ramming home another charge and for a split second had to turn away. It was then that the Newfoundland charged past him, and when David looked he saw that the bear was up and thudding toward him.

Its head was low, its mouth agape and David still had his priming to look to before he could meet the charge. During his Northland years he had shot many a bear. Some he had dropped without a sound, others had bellowed with rage; but this giant, as it closed, gave a throaty exhalation of hate and fury with every bound, and David realized that, even if he had had time to reload, he could not stop a creature of such terrible vitality.

A terrier, or one of the smaller Indian hunting dogs, would have employed worrying tactics, but Black Boy met the charge head on, hurling himself solidly against the rippling muscles of the bear's huge chest. Even if his teeth had not been old and blunted, he never could have gripped it by the throat and his weight was trifling against the impact of that hurtling body.

David saw the bear swerve. Somehow Black Boy had got a hold on the furry neck and the bear must rear to shake him off. Desperately David finished reloading. But now, for fear of hitting his dog, he dare not fire. Then a paw flashed up and Black Boy was crashed with sickening force against the face of a rock ten feet away. Even as David fired he was dimly aware that Black Boy was trying to close again. But his hind-quarters were limp and trailing. As he struggled to drag himself to the attack, David took aim at the exposed throat of the enemy. The ball, striking upward between the cleft of the lower jaws, shattered the animal's brain and it toppled limply forward.

David ran to where his dog was lying. In the dusk, the injuries were hard to see. But Black Boy, his back already broken, and his shoulder ripped open by the sweeping claws, tried to speak to him. David held him in his arms. He could feel the blood soaking his buckskin jacket, ebbing warm against his skin. The contorted body moved slightly within his arms. Then with a contented, long-drawn-out sigh, the old dog died.

CHAPTER TWENTY

Sorrowfully David Thompson
buried his faithful old comrade in a clump of pines on the
slope overlooking Fairford House. He and Black Boy had
come a long way together since they had hunted small game
at French Creek. It seemed to David a long time indeed since
he had been a raw apprentice and Black Boy a lumbering,
high-spirited pup. Since then they had roamed half a continent, had hunted moose and caribou and seen the buffalo in
countless thousands. They had gone through good times and

186

bad times together, and never once had the Newfoundland failed him. And at the last, his dog, in his old age, had died that he might live. It had been a tragic and yet an heroic parting.

During succeeding days when David hunted alone, the continued dearth of game and the departure of all Indian hunting parties from the country around the junction of the Reindeer and the upper Churchill made it plain that Fairford House must be abandoned in favor of newer ground. So, when at last Malcolm and his four canoes appeared, the young Scot had no sooner stepped ashore before David was suggesting that no stores be unloaded and that they proceed without delay to a likely trading point he had prospected on the west side of Reindeer Lake.

"Not so fast, Dave, not so fast!" Ross laughed. "Tell me first about your journey. Did you succeed?"

David nodded. "I've already sent an Indian down to York with my report. Now I'm eager to hear what Mr. Colen will have to say about our opening up the Athabasca route."

"Aye. But that's a piece of news you'll have to get later. The staff were still awaiting his return from England when I left York Factory. So we can't be sure of anything until the packet Indians come with our dispatches."

During succeeding days, while they completed plans for the new post on Reindeer Lake, Malcolm kept recalling items of talk he had picked up at York. To scores of company employees, separated for months from others of their kind, this headquarters fort was a clearing house for news of all sorts. Here, for generations, men and boys had met after a winter in the wilds, old comradeships were renewed, news from families in Scotland and England exchanged and the hopes and plans of their lives discussed.

"The staff are looking for great changes after Colen returns,"

187

Malcolm said. "Some think he'll have had such a dressing-down from the governors that he'll come back with his tail between his legs."

"What does Alf Robinson think?" David asked, throwing a hitch over the bale he was lashing.

"Oh, you know Alf! Always looking on the dark side. He feels sure the factor's managed to pull the wool over the governors' eyes again."

"If only we had governors in London with experience of this country," David said. Then with a grin: "Oh well, you're headed for promotion, Malcolm. Wait till you're called to London and appointed to the board."

"Aye, wait!" Malcolm answered with a wry chuckle. "Like as not I'll spend my days doing what I'm doing now. I've not the book learning. But you, with your surveying—you're the one who has the chance to sit some day with the nobs in London."

David shouldered his pack. There may have been a time when, like many another young apprentice, he had entertained such dreams. But that time was past. This vast Northland had set its seal upon him. For him there were no backward looks. This was his home.

Malcolm paused in his work and watched the short, sturdy figure going down the bank toward the waiting canoes. In their years together, the young Welshman's deliberate, self-contained manner had often puzzled him. "Koo-koo-sint," Ross mused. "The-Man-Who-Looks-at-the-Stars. Sometimes I think he'll reach them, too."

In reedy bays along the Churchill the wild geese were congregating for the great migration southward, and the first frosts had tinted birch and willow and poplar leaves by the time the start was made. At nights, camping along the Reindeer, they could hear the foxes yapping on the distant ridges.

Another winter was approaching and, at night, when they squatted around the big fire with their canoemen, David's active mind was on further explorations during the winter— the unknown country north of Reindeer Lake, perhaps, or some alternate route, so that in future the brigades of canoes which were bound to travel to the Athabasca could avoid the canyons of Black River in which he and his two Indians had almost met their death, for it seemed a certainty now that his report would result in great changes being made in company policy. After all, Factor Colen was but one against many. The Athabasca report was bound to strengthen the hands of the chief inland, Longmore, Oman, Philip Turnor and the rest. The days of marking time in the dreary Muskrat Country were finished and done with. Now Kozdaw and Paddy were waiting at the abandoned Fairford House to guide the packet Indians up Reindeer Lake. When the latter arrived, they would be bringing orders on which the future of Malcolm and himself would depend for years to come.

Sheltered bays near the new site on Reindeer Lake were being coated with thin ice at nights by the time the party was well at work, falling and hewing timbers for their cabins. According to the Indians, this would be the coldest winter in many years and, if they wanted to have everything snug, there was no time to lose. Then one sparkling afternoon a shout went up. The mail canoe was coming!

Twenty minutes later, standing among the chips where he had been hewing, the autumn air spicy with freshly-cut jack-pine, David took the two letters which were for him. One was from his mother in London. The other bore the company's official seal.

David opened the latter first. Sure enough, it was from Factor Colen. His orders were curt and final. David Thompson was to cease forthwith all surveys and explorations and devote his full energies to trade!

David sat down suddenly on the log he had been hewing. He found it hard to speak.

"Alf was right," Malcolm burst out when he had read the letter. "Can't you see Colen in London when the governors had him on the carpet! 'Yes, my lords; no, my lords; very good, my lords'—more mealy-mouthed than ever? But when he's safely back at York—the big toad in the little puddle—then that's another story." Savagely, in disgust, Malcolm drove his axe-blade deep into the log. "How I hate a man who says one thing and means another!"

This, David knew, was what Colen had been doing for years; appearing to the directors to be bowing to their wishes for westward exploration, yet all the time plotting to divert men and supplies into the Muskrat Country—the area under his direct control.

Malcolm scowled at the letter again. "It's a bitter pill, Dave, but he's got you cornered this time. It's a case of knuckle under or get out." He hesitated. "Which will it be?"

David leaned forward, elbows on knees, his square, capable hands relaxed and dangling, staring at the litter of pine chips. To Malcolm, outraged to the limit of endurance by Colen's duplicity, his partner's silence suggested a meek acceptance of this crowning injustice. "Man alive!" he exploded. "Say something. After this, your next move should be plain enough."

David rose slowly, spat on his hands and reached for his axe. "The next move is to get the roof on this house," he said. "Time enough to chart my course of action when we're secure against the winter."

Malcolm stared. Yet somchow this was very like the David Thompson he knew. David was now well on in his twenties, but even in his beginning apprentice days he had shown himself to be the sort who, in fair weather or foul, kept what was called "an even keel." A warm smile crossed Malcolm's intent, strong-featured face. "You're a cool one," he commented.

"If I didn't know how your heart is set on exploration, I'd be tricked into thinking you don't much care."

David shot him a look. His round, ruddy face with its snub nose made him seem more boyish than his years. But his steady eyes and the set of his rather wide mouth indicated plainly enough that Colen had yet to impose his plans on him. Actually, David was so wrought up he dare not trust himself to speak.

At every turn Factor Colen had deceived or thwarted him. As a pawn in Colen's game, he had been deprived of the priceless instruction Philip Turnor wanted him to have; there had been those next-to-useless winters in the Muskrat Country; when Colen had pretended to endorse the Athabasca exploration and had at the same time schemed to have it end in disaster by withholding men and outfit, David had felt he had known the limit in double-dealing. Now, on top of it all, a tyrannical order!

To all this was added something greater than personal disappointment, though that alone all but overwhelmed him. David Thompson knew, with unalterable certainty, that obedience to this last order meant the ruin of his career, as he had tried to shape it. Colen had maneuvered him into a position where he must resign himself to the life of a trader—or become an out-and-out rebel. From here on, there could be no compromises, no second chances.

Yet westward, controlled by his company, lay half a continent, practically unknown. The Rockies he had scouted from west of Buckingham House and from Piegan encampments; the North whose threshold he had seen when he fought through to the Athabasca—these were only fringes of a vast and waiting land which Colen and others in high places wanted to lock against all but those who would meekly serve such feudally-minded overlords. And the sting and torturing disappointment were the more bitter because, with his mapping

191

skill, he held in his own hand the key to unlock these areas for coming generations.

Now that his family's situation was improving, his mother and sister would remain in England but, recalling the slums of his boyhood where countless unfortunates possessed not one foot of God's green earth to call their own, Colen's greedy scheming seemed, more than ever, an evil thing. Furs and unbridled exploitation of the Indians were all Colen and his kind wanted. But to David this Canada-to-be meant vastly more. Already his diaries had noted the richness of the prairies, the forests and mineral wealth. The dispossessed of the Old World would be coming to America. Not all the Colens in the world could hold them back.

In their simple way, his Indian friends believed he could read the future in the stars. Now he was reading a future they could not know about. He had reached the parting of the ways. His future and this country's were one. Betraying that, he would betray all who should one day come in and possess it.

But until the new post had been made snug against the winter he declined to speak of the Colen letter again.

That winter was one of the coldest ever known in Western Canada and for humans and wild creatures alike, famine stalked the land.

"Our whole dependence for food was on our set nets and what little Deer's meat the Chepawyans could bring us," David wrote. "The fishery during the short open season was somewhat successful for white fish, but they were not of the best quality. But when the lake became frozen over, as usual the fish shifted their ground, and all we could procure was a bare subsistence. . . . This great, deep lake, 230 miles in length by 80 to 100 miles in width, was entirely frozen over. In the course of the winter the ice of the lake became five to six feet deep, and on the following year, the first water seen along the shore was on the 5th of July."

192

It was on a bitter night that, sprawled before their clay and stone fireplace, David told his partner of his decision.

"We've had our ups and downs together, Malcolm," David began soberly. "I've thought this matter over from all sides."

Malcolm rolled over and sat up. "Aye," he said, and waited.

"Now I know what I must do. It's a hard choice, Malcolm. I'm out of my apprenticeship. I'm leaving the company. I'm going to offer my services to the Nor'westers."

Malcolm Ross showed but slight surprise. It was the obvious move for one cornered as was his friend, and yet, now that David had put his decision in words, it seemed an anti-climax. "I'm going to offer my services to the Nor'westers." Variously phrased, the Scot had heard that decision from other lips. And usually there was a tinge of desperation or of defeat about it. Able and bold employees of the company had made it. But all too often it was the decision of the less capable and the malcontents. It was not that, even for an instant, Malcolm's belief in his friend wavered. David could succeed where many others failed. It was simply that it hurt him to realize that this tried and able comrade of his had been forced, by Colen's scheming, to make the same decision as these others, and almost in their very words.

"They'll engage you, Dave, without a doubt," Malcolm said at last.

"I can only hope so. For if not—" There was no need to finish the sentence. Both knew what too often happened to those who rebelled under company rule and later found their services were not wanted by the Nor'westers. The record was plain enough in the Muskrat Country and more so in the West and North. These misfits were sometimes driven to live the life of outlaw traders. The hands of both the great companies were against them, and theirs against the companies. Knowing this, the natives, too, suspected them. Grudges and feuds which the natives could not hold with safety against the powerful companies were sometimes visited upon these luckless ones.

"It will be different with you," Malcolm ventured. "You have your navigation."

The flames sent light and shadow dancing on the hewn logs of the little room. Outside in the darkness, the north wind's moan echoed in the stunted pines, and from a hundred miles to north and south came the muffled cannonading of the settling ice.

Malcolm stirred the fire and stared into the flames. "Say the word and I'll make the venture with you," he stated finally.

David shook his head. "It would be grand—just grand—to go together," he said. "But you know the chances. It's me more than you Colen's gunning for. No need for both of us to go. I may be jumping from frying-pan to fire, for all I know."

Now that the time of parting had come, it was difficult to keep emotion down. Malcolm swallowed hard. Then, turning, he thrust out his hand. "I wish you well, Dave," he managed.

Outside, west across the muskeg, a lone wolf howled. In spite of the fire, it suddenly seemed cheerless and bleak in the low-walled room.

Under date of May 23rd, 1797, the following entry was made in David Thompson's notebook:

*"This day left the services of the Hudson's Bay Company.
. . . May God Almighty prosper me."*

CHAPTER TWENTY-ONE

DAVID THOMPSON had grown from boyhood to early manhood in the services of the Hudson's Bay Company. What were his thoughts as he mushed southward, day after day, over the snow crust of that late spring?

During his thirteen years since leaving the Gray Coat School, he had traveled in all about nine thousand miles by canoe, on foot and on horseback. He had made numerous surveys and astronomical observations, and with Philip Turnor's aid was well advanced in the science of navigation. Few men grown old in the company's service had accomplished as much.

And now that he had broken with his employers, what assurance had he that the Nor'westers would engage him? Suppose his maps had not reached the proper hands in London? Colen would stop at nothing which advanced his own ends. What if, to cover his scheming, he had destroyed those maps?

From about eleven in the morning until the sun declined, the icy crust became so weakened that David's snowshoes broke through at every step. "The bottom gone out of the trail," Mitchell Oman used to call it in exasperation. However, in all except the very worst weather, David kept traveling, making slow progress during the daytime but putting swift miles behind him after the crust had set for the evening. Time and again, his snowshoe fillings chafed and broke from constant rubbing on the sharp crust. Then squatting on his heels, he would pluck out the main filling, splice it, and weave a four- or six-bar filling, as Young Otter had taught him that winter which now seemed so long ago.

Young Otter, Paddy, Kozdaw, the friendly Indians with whom he had hunted at York, old Saukamappee, and all those others who had accepted him, taught him, befriended him— where were they now? Had they forgotten the white one, Koo-koo-sint? No, they would not have forgotten, and in camps and wigwams he would never see again they would smile, recalling his first ineptitudes and remembering the comradeships of trail and portage. And Sam McPherson—?

It startled him, traveling on alone, to find he did not want to think too often about Sam. Twelve years, wasn't it, since Sam had fled south, away from injustice, hoping for another chance? And now, though the circumstances were different, he, who had pitied him, was being forced to do the same.

The barren country, with its rocks and stunted pines and miles of muskeg, was a fitting setting for the uncertainties and self-doubts which haunted David increasingly. If only he had someone to talk to! If only Black Boy were here! And if those maps had been destroyed, or kept from reaching the colonial office in London, what chance was there the Nor'-westers would even consider hiring him? His maps were his only testimonials—the very maps Colen and his friends did not want others to know existed!

Then, at one of his last camps before reaching the Pigeon River, he chanced to meet Roderick Mackenzie and Simon Fraser, two of the most active partners in the Nor'westers. This pair, traveling in state in their express canoes and with a retinue of servants, Scots and French Canadians, had assured him that the partners would grant him an audience when he reached Grand Portage, their headquarters at the west end of Lake Superior.

"We've heard o' you," the burly Fraser told him. But what they had heard, or from whom, he did not say. And though they would soon be returning to headquarters, David was not at all reassured by the fact that neither of them offered him transportation in one of their canoes.

A few days later David was astounded by what he found in a snug bay at the mouth of the Pigeon River. This imposing depot of those "sly wolves of the North," whose aggressive moves were working such havoc with the Hudson's Bay trade, was built of solid stone, not logs. And his first sight of the docks, piled high with bales of fur and trade goods, showed how successfully the traders from Montreal had been challenging the monopoly of the older company.

Immediately on arrival he had asked for an interview with the partners, and now, waiting in the yard, he tried to avoid thinking of how much that interview would mean to him. Simon Fraser's curt words kept him wondering. Had some, if not all, of his maps got past the governors to the Colonial

Office? Had any of the Nor'westers access to that office? What was it, actually, that Simon Fraser had heard?

A servant, idling near, spoke to him. "You've nothing half so grand as this at York," he said. "Yon's the powder magazine and jail." He pointed across at two stone buildings with iron-barred windows. "Behind you are the residences of the partners. The rest—storehouses, offices, servants' quarters and the like. And see the sentry, all in uniform, at the main gate. These Nor'westers! Fine, fighting gentlemen, all. The best's none too good for them."

"So it seems." There was an impression of feudal might, David thought, and of grimness, too, about this outpost of Canadian commerce. He could not recall ever feeling less sure of himself than at this moment. "I dare say the partners will send out word when I'm wanted." The nervousness in his voice made it a question.

"A young 'un like you must wait their pleasure," the servant answered, somewhat sharply.

David glanced down at his worn moccasins and patched buckskin leggings. Thirteen years in the wilds, with never a penny to spend on civilized clothes—why, he looked no more presentable than a *voyageur!*

"I used to think I had no nerves," he told himself. He who could crouch beside a game trail for hours waiting for the shot which would spell the difference between survival or starvation; who had infinite patience when it came to checking astronomical observations in a biting wind and at fifty below—here he was, pacing back and forth, unable to stand still a minute! "Get a grip on yourself," he thought. "The worst they can do is say no."

And if they did—what then? Had he jumped out of the frying-pan and into the fire, as his mother used to say? A tap on his shoulder made David turn sharply. "The partners will see you now," a clerk told him.

David took a deep, slow breath and squared his shoulders, then followed the clerk down a stone passageway and into the huge, high-beamed council hall. As the iron-studded door closed behind him, David was aware of the rumble of deep voices where the partners sat around a long table at the head of the room. On the wall behind he glimpsed several full-length portraits of partners in ruffles and scarlet coats.

"Stand here, before Sir Alexander," the clerk whispered; then backing deferentially away, he tiptoed from the room.

The man at the table nodded and studied David with shrewd, appraising eyes. He was Sir Alexander Mackenzie, discoverer of the mighty river which was now being called after him, the first man to cross the North American continent and reach the Pacific overland, and recently back from England after being knighted for it!

"I made it my business to study your maps in the colonial office, Thompson," the deep voice said, with a Highland burr. "You've done good work for our rivals. It is possible you may be able to do as much, or more, for us." He indicated a chair. "Sit down."

"The gentleman here at my right is Honorable William McGillivray," Sir Alexander went on. "These two you encountered on your way here, I'm told." He indicated his brother Roderick and Simon Fraser, soon to win fame as the discoverer of the Pacific's greatest salmon river.

The Honorable McGillivray stroked his beard. "Your coming has been timely, young man. Now listen closely. By the treaty ending the war with the American colonists, the international boundary was agreed to be from the northwest corner of Lake of the Woods to the source of the Mississippi—wherever that may be discovered to be. Later, the 49th parallel was accepted as the boundary between the Americans and Canada. The understanding was that all British trading posts south of that parallel must be withdrawn."

"Which last was none of our doing," Simon Fraser growled. "Trust an Englishman to make such a blunder! Yon treaty-makers were much too free with a domain which belongs to others, by right of exploration." Fraser's powerful jaw clamped angrily.

"Aye," Sir Alexander said, "but the treaty's made. It will not be altered. But as I just said, no one knows where the source of the Mississippi lies. The Americans surmise it must be somewhere close to the 49th parallel. I hope with all my heart they're right. For if not, by agreeing to set the boundary between the two countries at the 49th, we've surrendered a land larger than a score of Englands. All very friendly and no harm done—for the statesmen who agreed to it. But we of this company have our personal fortunes at stake."

Sir Alexander leaned forward and drummed his fingers on the table. "Here's the crux of the matter, Thompson. We Nor'westers have a rich trade in that great area. Have we lost our posts, or haven't we? That's the question. These high-and-mighty gentlemen, with their guesswork and wild approximations. But all this hits our pockets. No one knows where the 49th parallel lies. I'm ashamed to say so, but we of this company don't even know for certain the latitude and longitude of many of our trading posts in the disputed area. Not even those on the upper Red River. So you see, Thompson, until we have a true map—one which can never be disputed—our whole future in that rich country hangs in the balance."

He turned in his chair to face his partners. "Between us, all this is understood, of course. That's why I've been insisting this young surveyor is our man. In London they tell me that, with the possible exception of Philip Turnor, no one has made maps to equal his."

David found himself gripping the arms of his chair. In his wildest imaginings, he could think of no higher praise.

"Shall we proceed, gentlemen?" the Honorable McGillivray asked.

"Aye, aye," several voices answered.

McGillivray chose his words with care. "Thompson, we hereby engage you as astronomer and surveyor to the Nor'west Company." He named what to the penniless youth was a handsome salary. "When you have signed the agreement, we shall send orders to all our posts to give you all the help you need. We want the truth on this all-important matter. And we want it soon." Then, as an afterthought and one which was to trouble David in the strenuous months to follow: "For the sake of all concerned, it is to be hoped your findings will work to *our* advantage."

As David was ushered from the council hall he no longer thought of his poor appearance and wilderness garb. After the months and years of bafflement and doubt, this stroke of good fortune all but overwhelmed him. Official astronomer and surveyor to the Nor'west Company! The broken leg which had cost him his trip to the Athabasca with Philip Turnor—and given him his one great opportunity for training. His lonely nights with the Dollard sextant in the dreary Muskrat Country. Colen's scheming, Young Otter's help, the countless exercises worked out on paper and along rivers, on lakes and plains and frozen muskeg—the practice, practice, practice, and the high hope not surrendered! These and a host of other experiences all had their part in this hour of triumph. The tangled trails of chance had straightened and ahead his way ran clear and true!

Even while the documents were being signed and witnessed, news of the young stranger's appointment had reached the outer offices. The clerk who showed him out, the servant who had patronized him in the yard, the nods and smiles as he walked out of the fort and to his camp beside the river, all told him that he was recognized as a person of importance here.

And yet David knew this was no time for exultation. To locate the true source of the Mississippi might take years. And who could run a boundary line of perhaps a thousand miles as swiftly as the partners expected and not turn in slipshod work? And, besides all this, there were a dozen or more Nor'wester posts to be accurately established on a map.

Guesswork and approximation were not good enough, Sir Alexander had asserted. Not that David doubted his ability. But the partners demanded speed—and therein lay his danger. Their fortunes in all that area were at stake. And though they were giving him his great chance, these hard-living, hard-fighting men had the reputation of being ruthless with anyone who failed them.

Early in August David stowed his precious instruments into one of the canoes of the Swan River brigade and began the long journey to the head of Lake Winnipegosis. While waiting at Grand Portage, he had availed himself of every chance to study the records and rough sketches showing the approximate location of the company's trading posts throughout all the area. But he had searched in vain for any reliable information which might guide him somewhere near the Mississippi's source. Every scrap of data which might possibly help him had been entered in his notebooks for future reference. But even granted that some of the locations of rivers and posts set forth in the records were roughly correct, the blank stretches on his sketches were appallingly large.

As the brigade traveled westward, haste—and ever more haste—was imperative for him, even more than for the *voyageurs*. Portage, pack and vicious whitewater were the daily lot of all. Head winds delayed them and so, at times, when there was moonlight, the beaver-tail paddles bit the water hour after hour, far into the night. Then weary and drenched with sweat, all would go ashore on some point, a fire would be kindled, a *regale* would be rationed out, and the exhausted forms of the canoemen would be stretched in sleep around the blaze.

But as they progressed ever deeper into the area which must be mapped, there was not much opportunity for sleep in David Thompson's case. On countless nights, first in the Muskrat Country and later farther west and north, he had fixed his location by the stars. Now, during the brief periods for rest, he was doing it again.

With correct latitude and longitude to work from, he made the base points of his map as he traveled. And in daylight, his compass and his uncanny sense of direction and rate of travel helped him sketch in the waterways between each successive point. Week after week he was pushing back the boundary of the unknown.

But it was gruelling work. Once, long past midnight, as he brought his instruments back to camp, he saw that Indians from two canoes had landed and come to share the fire. David was stepping over his sleeping canoemen when a blanket-hooded figure in the shadows stirred.

"Greetings, Koo-koo-sint!" a soft voice said.

David peered across the dwindling fire. "Who are you?" he asked in Chepaywan.

The unknown one pushed the charred ends of firewood together, and as they broke into flame David saw he was a slender young man not much older than himself.

"We hunted together," the Indian told him, "but that was many moons ago."

Weary, half dead from lack of sleep, David blinked. "Young Otter!"

His comrade of Churchill days smiled. "My friend!"

Squatting beside the fire, they talked. It was not an Indian's way to come straight to the point. They talked of many things. "Remember Scar Face?" Young Otter asked. "He came this way. Have you had word of him?"

"In the Muskrat Country, yes. One of your people told me he had been seen at Grand Portage. That was years ago. I'm ashamed of myself that I did not think to ask." The sudden realization that in the press of work he had forgotten poor Sam brought a twinge of conscience. "Have you?"

Young Otter shook his head. Already the stars were less bright to the east and north. The time had come to tell why he had trailed David all this way. "Take me with you, Koo-koo-sint, wherever you are going."

"And leave your people?" David jerked his head toward the other Indians sleeping by the fire.

"They are not my own people. It is by chance we travel together."

"But your family? By now you will have married and—"

"My wife is dead, and our little son went with her to the spirit land. On the Churchill last winter there was the white man's sickness. I am alone. On the Churchill I heard you had come south. I followed because I want to be with you. My heart is heavy when I stay in the old places. I want to go with you."

David was slow to answer. "I am traveling to lands I do not know. I have a great work to do and it may be years before I come back."

"These others, they may leave you, but I would not leave a man who is my friend. Take me with you, Koo-koo-sint."

"And why not?" David said decisively. This was not as in the old days in the bay country. Here he could choose his men. Had not the partners given him full authority? "It's good to have you, Young Otter. There will always be a place for you in my canoe."

CHAPTER TWENTY-TWO

DAVID THOMPSON had no cause
to regret the decision he made that night. No *voyageur* of the
brigade excelled Young Otter as a navigator of rapids, none
bore more cheerfully the rigors of the trail, and certainly
among all that hardy band none so much as equaled him in
hunting. Weeks later, when the brigade split up and David
had but one canoe, Young Otter became his bowman. And
lucky was the moose or feeding deer which eluded his sharp
eyes from that vantage point in their long birchbark as the
craft nosed around a river's bend, or ghosted close inshore
along the reedy backwaters. Thanks, in large part, to Young

Otter, not a day was lost in seeking food. The Thompson party lived off the country as it traveled, and for the first time in all his explorations David was able to devote his entire energies to mapping.

Late in November, when the party put up at Assiniboine House, David had fixed the positions of all the Nor'wester posts on the Assiniboine and the Red Deer, and mapped these rivers to their sources. It was an encouraging start.

But it was only a start, and by this time winter had come and the risky journey across the plains to fix the true position of the upper Mississippi was still to be attempted. Yet no sooner had John McDonnell, factor at Assiniboine House, learned of David's plan than he warned him not to go on.

"I tell you, Thompson," the factor insisted, "it is highly dangerous. One of my scouts came in only last night with word that the Sioux are on the warpath. Some of their warriors have been killed by the Mandans of the Missouri and the Sioux blame us."

"Because you furnished them with firearms?" David asked. He recalled the attitude the Piegans had taken years before when he had hinted of his desire to cross their domain and make contact with the Kootenays. There could have been no clearer evidence that he had reached the farthest outpost of exploration.

"Aye," McDonnell answered, "that's their reason. And they have taken an oath to waylay and scalp any white who ventures westward. You're not faced with any band of docile wood Indians now. These Sioux are vengeful. I tell you, man, it's suicide to go."

But the Nor'westers' future, as well as his own, was at stake and David knew he must make the attempt. With the recent boundary settlement placing a large part of the Montreal company's fortune very much in doubt, more than ordinary chances must be taken. He had seen enough of the partners at

Grand Portage to know they were not the sort to accept excuses. But it was under protest that the factor at Assiniboine House furnished David's party with what was needed and a few days later watched the young explorer lead them westward toward the treeless plains.

Fighting blizzards day after day and at night huddling in cheerless camps, David kept on the course he had charted. Under lowering skies he was unable to take observations on sun and stars and so must travel by dead reckoning.

It was as they neared the Dog Tent Hills that they sighted the dreaded Sioux. The date, according to David Thompson's diary, was the day before Christmas, and the time about two o'clock in the afternoon. After weeks of battling wind and snow, sunrise had brought a southerly breeze. And though only four days previously David's thermometer had registered forty-one degrees below zero, the morning had dawned comparatively mild. In preparation for their dash across hostile country, several of the hand toboggans had been loaded with fire-killed willow, a wood which gave good heat and yet no telltale smoke. Powder horns and shot pouches had been replenished, musket primings seen to, and at half-past eight that morning the party set out in single file.

Lalonde, a veteran *voyageur,* broke trail. Next, pulling the first toboggan, came Young Otter, willing as always, yet somewhat out of his element so far from his native forest country. Behind Young Otter, David mushed. He had just taken a compass sight on the highest butte of the Dog Tent Hills— one that stood a good two hundred feet higher than the surrounding plain. Swinging along on his snowshoes, he kept constant lookout. In the deeper gullies of the hills, purple shadows lingered. In others, reached by the sun, the light was dazzling and brought out the leafless oaks and stunted elms starkly against the snow.

The Sioux could not have chosen a more cunning place

for an ambush. With eyes narrowed against the increasing glare, the men kept a sharp watch on the skyline.

"I see nothing, m'sieu," Lalonde called back.

"Nor I," David answered. Nevertheless, he stepped out of the broken trail and, while the other sleds filed past, took out his brass telescope and trained it on the butte.

"Down! Down on your stomachs, all of you!" he shouted an instant later.

Every man flung himself into the snow. Tense minutes passed and still the butte seemed quite deserted. "Wriggle deeper—and keep your heads down," David cautioned. And to the man behind him: "Pass the word along." Then he trained his telescope on the skyline and watched. In a moment his suspicions were confirmed. A number of horsemen appeared against the sky. Through the telescope they seemed so near that David could make out the eagle feathers of their war bonnets and the long tails of their ponies streaming in the breeze. Tensely, he told Lalonde what he saw.

"If they have seen us, we are done for, surely," the *voyageur* muttered. "But the sun, she helps us!" Now he knew why their leader had kept swinging south that morning. For hours he had chosen a course which kept their shadows, thrown by the low, midwinter sun, stretching always toward the butte. In this way the folds of the hills stood out sharply for them while, for any watcher from the top, the sunset must surround them with a blurring, protective glare.

For a good ten minutes David kept the Sioux focused in his lenses. Then, as suddenly as they had appeared, the scouts wheeled and vanished. Half an hour later, from their hiding places in the snow, the Thompson party saw a hundred or more horsemen ride down the far shoulder of the hill and strike north and west across the plains.

Grins of relief showed on the weathered faces of the *voyageurs*. "War parties must travel light," one of them exulted. "This bitter weather has been harder on them than us. We will see the Mississippi yet."

Christmas Day was spent in traveling, but on the twenty-seventh the party was weather-bound again. "Early a terrible storm from SSW, and raged all day," David recorded. "The sound of the wind was like the waves of the sea on a lee shore.

"December 28th, a fine, clear, mild day, thank God," his diary continued. "At 7½ we set off, taking firewood and tent-poles with us and proceeded S 40 W 22 miles and at 4½ p.m. pitched our tent to pass the night. . . . We saw but few bison and about an hour before we put up saw ten or twelve horsemen far on our left. A fine, clear night."

It was on the last day of 1797 that they reached the upper Missouri and were welcomed in the commodious, clay-domed dwellings of the Mandans' principal village—dwellings so unlike those of his people that Young Otter marveled.

That evening, as David sat beside the chief's fire and recorded the day's events, he thought of his mother and the children. With money coming in, this Christmas might have been a merry one for them. A goose, perhaps, and pudding. Had the presents he put in the mail at York Factory ever reached them? His sister would be into her teens by now. If only he could have a picture of her! "And why not?" he thought. "A painting, with Mother." When he drew his first salary he would see what could be done about that. Or, better still, a few years from now, what was there to stop him setting the family up in Montreal? Other Nor'west officials did it. If his work on this survey satisfied the partners, there was bound to be promotion, more money. They had waited long enough for him to make his mark. They should have nothing but the best! It gave him a particular kind of pleasure to think that the Thompsons, as a family, would become Canadians. "I'll do it, I really will," he decided.

The Mandans were the first Indians David had lived with who had permanent houses, tilled the soil and harvested corn, pumpkins and other crops against the winter. Their mode of life interested him greatly, but with his great task still unfulfilled he must push on. Early in the New Year he marshaled his party, and on the third of February was safely back at Assiniboine House.

"Thanks be, you won through safely. I feared for you," Factor McDonnell greeted him. "Now you can rest up here until the breakup."

"Only long enough to prepare my maps and notes so they can be taken to Grand Portage by your spring brigade."

McDonnell chuckled and shook his head in mock despair. "What bee have you in your bonnet this time? You ambitious ones—everlastingly on the move!"

"And why not?" David grinned back. "Late winter is the prime time for traveling." He hesitated to disclose the cause for his uneasiness.

The truth was that his dash to the Missouri and back had revealed that even more of their posts than the partners suspected must lie south of the international boundary line. This fact would hit them hard. Sir Alexander Mackenzie, the Honorable McGillivray and their associates were traders, first and foremost. When they realized how many of their posts must be surrendered to the Americans, they might well decide that, to recoup this heavy loss, new posts must be set up at once north of the 49th parallel. This, of course, would mean greater competition than ever with the Hudson's Bay Company.

But it would mean something else, as well. It would mean that every experienced officer under the partners would be concentrated on the task of making this competition pay dividends. It could—and probably would—mean that he himself would be commanded to drop his mapping and join in an intensified drive for furs. If the partners came to this decision, the chances were heavily against his being able to devote full time to his surveying for years to come.

Working over his drafting board in the factor's quarters, David viewed this possibility from all angles. And the more he thought of it, the more inevitable it became. But there was one way out. It lay completely in his hands.

"Suppose," he thought, "that I wait until the entire survey is completed? Suppose I don't send in this map with the spring brigade? Suppose I take it to Grand Portage myself after I've seen the country south of forty-nine?" It was a temptation. "For," he reasoned, "it may take months to fix the true source of the Mississippi."

There was no denying that in delaying like this he could find a certain amount of justification in the wording of the orders the partners had given him. They may not have intended him to take it that way but, after all, with his career at stake—

Below this surface reasoning, words which Philip Turnor had spoken to him, as he lay in that fort on the plains with a broken leg, returned to trouble him. *"I admire a man who'll follow truth, no matter where it leads him."* And when Mr. Turnor had given him his precious sextant: *"You can thank me by doing honest work. I may be wrong, but somehow I believe you're of the breed who will."*

When he had lain in his bunk at Manchester House, he had found only inspiration in those words. But now it seemed that Philip Turnor, in his devotion to the truth, was warning him.

CHAPTER TWENTY-THREE

Dᴀᴠɪᴅ Tʜᴏᴍᴘꜱᴏɴ was not conscious of making any sudden, clear-cut decision about his course of action for the coming weeks. Perhaps it was because from early boyhood, and later from his hard-won training as a scientist, a pattern of honest behavior had been set. But whatever the motive, he found himself working longer hours and with intensified application to complete the first part of his all-important map so that it would be ready for the partners by the time of the spring councils at Grand Portage.

With this decision arrived at, a second one became increasingly apparent. This was that in haste—and ever more haste—

lay his assurance of success. By far the greater portion of his mission had yet to be fulfilled. Next season might be too late. The partners were practically certain to assign him to help wage the war for trade, once they realized how great was the area they would be surrendering to the Americans. In a matter of months he must complete a map which, by ordinary standards, should have taken several years. So as soon as his map and report were sealed, he warned Lalonde, Young Otter and the rest to stand in instant readiness to take the trail.

The ensuing weeks were strenuous ones. Urging on his Indian guide and three *voyageurs,* he completed his survey up the Red River in record time. No sooner was that accomplished than their dog team was speeding down the Assiniboine. Ice jams and heavy snows slowed them, but by the seventh of March they reached the junction of that river and the Red. Here David fixed the true position of what, generations afterward, would be the city of Winnipeg.

By the twenty-fifth of March he had determined the position of the 49th parallel. This required very careful checking. All south of it had become American territory and as he studied the draft of his map David was appalled by the implications of his survey. What would the partners say of his work—and of him—when they realized how much of the country over which they had ruled would have to be surrendered to the Americans?

What was it the Honorable McGillivray had said that day at Grand Portage? "For the sake of all concerned, it is to be hoped your findings will work to *our* advantage." It was a natural enough remark under the circumstances. But now it took on a sinister significance. Sir Alexander Mackenzie had pointed out to the partners that their personal fortunes were at stake if the surveys went against them. "And they *are* against them," David thought.

Here he was, the person sent out to protect their interests, proving it! Such a menace to his future in the Nor'west Company was so obvious. Why hadn't he seen it before? Suppose they refused to accept his findings? It would be years before an international survey could be organized and sent out. And in those years, aggressive fur traders like the Nor'westers could reap a fortune.

That night, in a windswept camp in the lee of gaunt willow clumps, David Thompson faced yet another decision. "But facts are facts. It's what they sent me out to find, and they'll have to face the music."

Face the music! How clearly he remembered when he had used that phrase to Sam. Instead, Sam had become a fugitive. What had become of his unfortunate friend, he probably would never know, but in his own case David saw what he must do. For what would Philip Turnor think of him if, like Governor Hearne, and Pound, too, he tried to twist the facts to suit his own ends? "It's all or nothing now," he decided. His trails and survey lines had always run true. They would continue to do so, no matter where they led him.

The sun was daily becoming stronger, the ice more treacherous, yet the party pressed on until they reached Red Lake Falls—still another post which he had to report must be abandoned.

"Winter travel is at an end, m'sieu," Baptiste Cadotte, the Red Lake factor cautioned. "If you strike eastward now, you will find yourself in trouble."

"Perhaps so," David admitted. He dare not give Cadotte any hint of what would soon be the fate of his post; nor had he authority to reveal the reason behind his seemingly reckless haste. Yet finding the true source of the Mississippi was an undertaking which could not wait. "I'll have to risk it just the same, Cadotte," he added.

Cadotte flung up his hands. "On your head be it. You young ones! Only never say I did not warn you."

With the assistance of Young Otter, David had already located an Indian guide familiar with the flat, low country to the eastward. Only when Cadotte had read the written authority from the partners for Thompson to draw what stores he needed from any of their posts would he consent to outfit the survey party. Immediately the sled was loaded the start was made.

In these last months, David Thompson had added immense areas to the map of the known world. But time was running short. Spring was upon him and very soon now the partners would be assembling at Grand Portage to decide policy for the coming year. Very soon, too, they would have to face the unpleasant truth as revealed to them by his Assiniboine House report.

In spite of difficulties, the undertaking had been going like clockwork. Lalonde and Young Otter were willing and loyal, and what grumbling occurred among the others was never serious. The first day out from Red Falls began deceptively crisp and fine. But at noon the thaw caught them. The woven *babiche* in the toes and heels of their snowshoes clogged, the rawhide main fillings sagged, and each step became an effort. That night their guide deserted them, yet next day they struggled on. Then a violent thunderstorm broke, and by the fourth day the sled was floating and the men floundering knee deep in slush and snow water. The whole area had turned to swamp. Each man had to cross every pond and winding stream armed with a long pole held crossways to prevent him from disappearing entirely when he broke through the rotted ice. Finally David had to admit defeat. Days later they straggled back to Red Lake Falls.

Their rest there was brief, however. "I must have a canoe," David told the factor.

Cadotte shrugged. "Very well, my friend. But you must sign for it. I accept no responsibility for this madness." Though intensely jealous of any challenge to his authority, the French-Canadian factor was a kindly man. And as he regarded the weary young surveyor and his exhausted helpers, he made a final effort to induce them to rest at the post until the treacherous spring was over. "In these parts, the summer is best for traveling," he urged. "Only remain with me until then and I will—"

David thanked him and shook his head. He seemed as determined as ever, yet it was the gesture of a troubled and utterly weary man. The old hurt in his leg had been bothering him again and he knew that if he made a second attempt eastward there would be no dry camps, dry clothes or decent food for weeks on end.

"Why not sleep on your decision?" Cadotte urged. "Lalonde here is a good man—none better. But look at him! Sleep has claimed him even as we talk."

Lalonde, sprawled on the bearskin before the fire, rolled lazily onto one elbow, rubbed his eyes, yawned ponderously, and winked slyly in David's direction. "These factors are all the same. They like to live softly. They grow paunches. It makes them as indolent as the *seigneurs* of old Ke-bec!"

Many a time when journeying by trail or canoe, David had marveled at the gay spirit which was displayed by men like Pierre Lalonde under hardship. Never for them the fame, the rich reward. Down-river to the Arctic, through the mountain gorges and overland to the Pacific with Mackenzie, these nameless ones could look forward to none of the world's acclaim which fortified the hearts and steeled the wills of their adventurous leaders. Privation and grueling toil crippled and aged them before their time. Yet their jaunty spirits seldom wavered. David thought then, as he had thought many times before and would again, how true

216

it was that no one race of men possessed all the courage in the world; how true it was that all were "members one of another" and how each in his own way contributed to the well-being of all. Here tonight when, baffled and weary, the undaunted spirit of this unschooled man gave him the courage to go on, David resolved that—be their fate success or failure—he at least would not forget.

A fresh start was made the next morning. Hauling the canoe over the rotting ice with the sled lashed under it, they paddled across the open leads, then mushed and hauled again. Day after day, with infinite toil, they made their way from lake to lake. After nineteen such days they came to Turtle Lake.

From a soggy main camp, David took Young Otter and Lalonde and explored the surrounding lakes and ponds. Miserable as their condition was, nothing could be left to guesswork or to chance. With that sixth sense of the born geographer, David knew that somewhere in this area was the Mississippi's source. It was after repeated side trips that he decided Turtle Lake itself was the spot he had come so far to find. Many years later, American surveyors fixed the Mississippi's source as being in a small lake hard by. But for all practical purposes David Thompson had solved that outstanding problem. He was the first to fix on any map the beginnings of the great river draining half a continent!

However, a daring journey still faced the party. The canoe was leaking badly. For many miles the low, level ground was no better than a swamp. Sluggish feeder streams writhed like snakes among the willow clumps and quaking knolls. "Brooks so winding," David wrote, "that after paddling for an hour we appeared to have made little or no progress." After the swift Canadian rivers, it was like floundering in some gigantic maze.

When the next post to be surrendered—Cass Lake—was

217

reached, they found themselves in even drearier country. Not a deer or a beaver was to be seen. Urged on by white traders, the Indians had killed them all and in so doing had worked their own ruin. Maple sugar, wild rice and coarse fish were their only food. Here the fat geese flew in safety, for the poverty-stricken Indians could no longer buy fire-arms, and in their scramble for easy money they had lost the art of making and using bows and arrows. "Like packet Indians, living off the posts," Young Otter said sadly. "But here the post has gone and they are left with nothing. They have forgotten how to help themselves. They will die and be forgotten."

Still fighting east, the party came at last to the shore of Lake Superior, near the spot where some day the city of Duluth would stand. Their canoe was in ruins, and though Young Otter searched all day he reported he could find neither birchbark nor pitch for patching it.

Lalonde, game to the last, sat on a beach log and shook his head. "To have come so far, and now—"

"Get the fire going," David said. "We'll camp. I'll walk the shore the other way and see what can be found."

A quarter of a mile away, where the beach ended in a rocky bluff, David was surprised to find a well-trodden path leading over the narrow ridge and down to a pleasant bay beyond. As he came to the shore, the sharp barking of a dog stopped him in his tracks. Then, proceeding cautiously, he reached a clearing. A small stream ran across the gently sloping ground. There was a cabin, with smoke rising from its clay and stone chimney. As he watched, a man came out. Calling the dog to heel, the man came part way down the path, then stopped and beckoned. David waved back and, as he approached, a strange feeling of excitement made him forget how tired he was. The man kept staring at him, then, as if drawn forward against his will, he took a few steps. Again he stopped. David began to wonder if, in his torn clothes and with his long hair, the stranger took him for an Indian or some half-breed derelict whose coming to this little homestead was far from welcome.

"Something told me it was you. Right from the first—when you stopped there on the beach, I— Dave, have you forgotten me?" The stranger turned his head and David saw the long, knotted scar.

Exhaustion, days of meager rations, the old hurt in his leg, suddenly combined to make David fear he was going to collapse. Like a man in a trance, he stood there, staring, his mind reaching out for words, discarding them, refusing to accept the evidence of his numbed senses.

"I'm glad you've come, Dave," Sam said. "Somehow I always thought you would."

It was foolish, and unmanly, and not like him at all—David knew that. But these days and weeks of fighting swamps and hunger, of lack of sleep, of taking observations or shooting the sun while the others drowsed beside their fires or sprawled on the moss to take their nooning, were all against him now. He felt a strange prickling in the corners of his eyes, and realized that tears—of relief, of joy, of a peculiar sort of vindication—were on the verge of falling.

"You're at the end of your tether, Dave," Sam was saying, and he pulled his friend's arm across his broad shoulders and led him to the cabin. "Sit you down. I'll make you a sup and bite."

David followed him with his eyes as he stirred the fire, brewed tea, and with his sheath knife sliced moosemeat from a haunch hanging, smoked and ready, from the rafters.

"You're not alone?" Sam asked. "You'll be traveling with a party?"

David pointed back over the rocks. "A small one. Young Otter, from Churchill, is the only one you know."

219

Sam lowered his head and shook it in the way he used to do when he was in doubt or faced with a decision. "Better not be telling him you've seen me. Though I'm a free man now, y'understand. I've got this homestead, do a bit of trapping and trading. I've saved my money and next year, if all goes well, I'll be starting in with sheep."

"Young Otter hasn't forgotten you, Sam. I know he'd like to see you. Look at this good place you've made. Know you're all right."

"He was one of the best, up there. But no, Dave. That part's all over and done with." He took the smoked haunch from its hook. "Take him this. Then, when you're a day's paddle down the lake, you tell him it's from me."

David went on eating, then told about their useless canoe.

"There'll be a canoe beached near your camp before daylight tomorrow morning. You're to take it, understand. My twenty-eight footer, rigged with sail and oars."

David was at a loss for words. "If I could pay you—"

"Now, none of that. I've done well here, like I told you. You'd do the same for me and—"

A long "hulloo" came from beyond the ridge. Unless the story of what had become of Sam McPherson, the runaway apprentice, was to be carried by Lalonde and his garrulous friends the length and breadth of the far country, David must go before they found him here. "I'll stow the meat in the bow of the canoe. And as to what you find on the beach come morning, that's a secret between us two," Sam said as David rose to go. Then with that distorted grin of his: "It wouldn't be the first one we've had—and kept, eh?"

David gripped his old schoolmate by the shoulders. "If only you knew how good this makes me feel! A place of your own. Something to work for—"

"And independence. Don't forget the independence. Why,

man! I'd laugh in his face if Governor Hearne offered to trade places with me now."

How much Lalonde knew, David could only guess, but at least he kept his suspicions to himself. At dawn, when the big canoe was discovered, he accepted it for what it was—a windfall. Like David, the veteran *voyageur* knew the long journey was nearing its climax and he was counting the days and hours until he would be back with his fellow Canadians, joking and talking French again.

Good sailing weather favored the explorers. When he had mapped this shoreline of the greatest body of fresh water in the world, David's survey would be completed. Helped by a following wind, Lalonde and the others laid aside their paddles. Exhilarated by these miles of blue water after weeks of dismal swamp, they would often burst into song. They even tried, with much hilarity, to teach Young Otter the opening lines of their favorite *"En Roulant Ma Boule."*

The high, birchbark stern raced and swirled before the breaking swells. There were good fish in plenty to be caught at each nightly camp. The sky was so clear that David was able to make accurate observations and fix points on his map to link compass bearings and notes of distances which he made almost continuously as they skirted the long shoreline. It was the seventh of June, and the stars were coming out when a few lights showed against the forest wall. With paddles flying, they hit the beach at Sault Ste. Marie. The epic journey was ended.

"No need to pitch the tent on so fine a night," Lalonde said.

"But we must have the best of cooking fires," David told him. "We'll look after that while you nip up to the fort. If the trade room's open, buy anything you fancy. Molasses, ship biscuit, raisins. Everything of the best. This is a night for feasting."

In a few minutes, Lalonde came racing back. "Good news! Two of the partners reached the fort this afternoon on their way to Montreal. I told the sentry you were here. The partners must see you now—at once."

Good news, was it? David thought as he got out his maps and notebooks. His far-flung survey was an accomplishment nothing could deprive him of. But the hard facts it proved were an altogether different matter. Would the partners dispute his findings, make him the scapegoat, and thus delay surrender of their posts while trade in those regions was intensified? To prevent his findings from breaking their monopoly, would they try to make a mere trader of him, as the Hudson's Bay Company had wanted to do? "The names?" he asked hurriedly. "You didn't find out their names?"

Lalonde shook his head. "The sentry said 'the partners want him' and I came running."

David scrambled up the bank. The sentry admitted him, escorted him across the yard, knocked, and David stepped into the lighted room. As the servant led him forward, the partners' backs were toward him. Then he saw it was Sir Alexander Mackenzie and the Honorable McGillivray who were rising from their chairs before the hearth.

Their cordiality as they shook his hand left David wondering. "You received my report from the Assiniboine?"

Sir Alexander nodded. "In time for our council at Grand Portage. We are now on our way to Montreal where our future strategy must be decided. Your first report upset our plans considerably, Thompson. Let us hope your final one tells a somewhat different story."

"I'm afraid it doesn't, sir." David gave the partners the straight, hard facts. Not a word was spoken as he opened his map and held it to the light for them to see.

Sir Alexander studied it with grim intensity, then rubbed his chin. The servant brought a small table and set candlesticks at either end. The map was laid on it and Mackenzie, on his feet now, bent over it, reading the neat, black lettering, tracing rivers, lakes and the chain of posts with his finger. McGillivray joined him. David could not see the expression on their faces. But as minutes passed and no word was spoken, he tried to brace himself for what was coming.

"Man alive!" Sir Alexander said suddenly. "Do you realize what you've done? In ten months you've mapped four thousand miles of country. That's more than could be expected of any other surveyor I know in two years, at least."

"Aye," McGillivray admitted. "But Red Lake and Cass Falls, too—that's a bitter pill to swallow."

Sir Alexander straightened. "We told him we wanted the truth, did we not? We wanted a man whose ability and, even more, whose integrity, we could rely on. Well, we got him. That should be plain as a pikestaff now."

"It is, and now we have his verdict, we'll abide by it."

"Precisely," Sir Alexander went on vigorously. "Not that these reports are quite what we expected. They go much farther than that. But it was true geography and not a deceptive tale we called for." He brought his hand down on the table. "I've seen with my own eyes what awaits us beyond the mountains and, as I've told the council more than once, the future of us men from Canada lies in the West and North. We're not Hudson's Bay men. Thompson's report should merely serve to spur us on." He laid his hand on David's shoulder. "Sit you down. You've established your reputation not only with our company, but in places far beyond. The night's still young and we have the future—ours and yours—to discuss."

Much later that night, after David had taken supper with the partners, he heard the sound of singing and knew it came from his campfire on the beach below. Now and then, during pauses in the talk, he could make out Lalonde's lusty voice. Young Otter, with his quiet smile, would be there. David could picture their faces in the leaping firelight, just as he had seen them in many wild and distant camps.

He knew now that this night was only the beginning. Across the plains, into the mountains and beyond, the West and North were waiting. It was all his country. Soon, when he had established the family in Montreal, it would be theirs as well. And Sam's, for America also had its great, untrammeled West. With French-Canadian and Indian friend, and those of many other races, they would go on, together.